BENTLEY BR2
World War 1 Rotary Aero Engine

The Author and Builder of the original one quarter scale Bentley B.R.2. rotary aero engine being presented with the Duke of Edinburgh Challenge Trophy at the 1982 Model Engineer Exhibition at Wembley, London by a former Prime Minister of the United Kingdom, Sir Harold Wilson.

This award is made to the overall winner from all the Gold Medal winners at the previous Exhibition. This is the first time that this Award has been taken out of the United Kingdom.

BENTLEY BR2

World War 1 Rotary Aero Engine

Building the
one quarter scale
working
replica

by L.K. BLACKMORE

Publisher's Note to the second printing: being essentially a steam man, I was somewhat suspicious when Lew Blackmore contacted me in 1987 suggesting I should sell copies of his book on building a Bentley BR2 Rotary engine, but was persuaded by his approach, and the fact that IC engines running on the S.M.E.E. stand at the Model Engineer Exhibition always drew large crowds (which had the benefit of protecting us, to some extent, from the resulting slipstream). The response to the book was very positive, which led to a steady and pleasurable correspondence with Lew, who came across as a very genuine and kind man, with an encyclopaedic knowledge of aircraft piston engines. He used this to write a biography of Harry Hawker - no mean achievement when Lew lived in Australia. In due course the Bentley book went out of circulation and our correspondence lapsed until September 1995 when Lew approached me about doing a second printing of the book. Sadly this resumption of contact with him did not last long, as he passed away on the 7th November 1995 from a serious illness, bravely fought. I hope that this second printing of his book, with the agreement of his Executors, and especially his wife Patricia, to whom all thanks are rendered, will be a fitting tribute to a fine man and a fine model engineer, who largely pioneered the building of large scale, scale working models of piston aircraft engines.

To my wife Patricia

Special thanks to:

Herb Malley, for his interest in the engine from its
very beginnings. His help, advice and proof reading have
been a major contribution.

Professor D.H. Chaddock, for his inspiration and help.

Michael White for guiding me through the publishing jungle.

British Library Cataloguing-in-Publication Data: a catalogue record of this book is held by the British Library.

ISBN 0 9519367 4 3

First edition published in Australia by Yalanga Pty. Ltd

The second (1996) and third (2002) editions published in Great Britain by:

Camden Miniature Steam Services,
Barrow Farm,
Rode, Frome,
Somerset. BA11 6PS

"Camden" stocks one of the widest selections of engineering, technical and transportation books to be found anywhere. Write to the above address for a copy of their latest Booklist.

WARNING: in this book the author and publishers are only passing on information on how readers can build and run a particular model. **Safety is your responsibility** and you must **always** be aware of the potential dangers inherent in using tools, machine tools and running your model.

Printed and bound by Salisbury Printing Ltd.

CONTENTS

The model Bentley B.R.2.

FOREWORD

When Mr. Blackmore showed me the model he had built of the Bentley B.R.2 Aero engine, and demonstrated it running, I was amazed in more ways than one.

To have made all the engine parts without the normal drawings and to a quarter scale was in itself an exceptional accomplishment, but then for the engine to start up with a flick on the propeller and run smoothly was almost unbelievable.

To me the model of the Bentley Rotary brought back a vivid memory and recollections of seventy years ago. As a young engineer, learning my profession at Vickers Limited, Crayford, England, working in probably the best equipped tool room in the U.K. with five hundred tool makers and two shifts, during the World War 1 period. I was given a drawing marked, "Secret A.R.1." (Admiralty Rotary). It was not until the advent of the Royal Air Force on April 1st, 1918, the name changed to B.R.1 (Bentley Rotary). The drawing was of a component to be used on the prototype engine which I later saw tested at Vickers.

The next co-incidence was toward the end of World War 1 when learning the theory of flying at the Royal Naval College, at Greenwich, I wrote a lengthy thesis together with drawings on the Clerget Rotary Aero engine which was similar to the B.R.1. At that time Bentley Rotary engines had not been installed in aircraft.

Yet another co-incidence, just prior to the Armistice I landed at an aerodrome in Cheshire where I saw the first Sopwith Snipes equipped with the B.R.2 engines, a photograph of which I have in my possession.

To further appreciate the excellent accomplishment of making this model is the fact that Mr. Blackmore, until his retirement had never turned his hand to model making, yet he has completed one of the most difficult projects in the form of this Rotary Aero engine.

Larry Hartnett,

Sir Laurence Hartnett

The quarter full size model Bentley B.R.2.

PREFACE

The idea of building a model of some vintage aero engine from the World War 1 era stemmed from the writer's interest in aviation generally. It was a kind of project not usually undertaken by model engineers, which made it more attractive.

The idea took shape after being invited by Professor Chaddock to attend a lecture to be given at the University of Loughborough in England by Mr. Donald Bastow. Mr. Bastow was closely associated with W.O. Bentley and has written a most authoritative book on Bentley's life, including the time he was involved with aero engine design and production during W.W.1. This lecture inspired me to adopt the B.R.2 as a most worthy project. Unfortunately there were no drawings of any kind to be found, and none have since been discovered.

The main source of information was the Air Ministry Publication which was simply a Handbook dealing with the B.R.2. It did however contain a cross section of the engine which it was hoped would be to scale. This proved to be the case, or very close to it. The only dimensions known with certainty were the bore and stroke and the whole design was reconstructed by measurement of the drawing and multiplying by the scale factor that had been determined. Once begun the project proved very challenging and one by one the design problems were solved and the design emerged. It has now been generally accepted as an authentic scale reproduction, for which a full set of drawings has been made.

Right from the time it was ready to run it has been easy to start and has been seen running by literally thousands of people who are astounded that the whole engine rotates.

It created great interest and was exhibited at the Model Engineer Exhibition in London in 1981 where it was awarded the Gold Medal in its class.

Gold Medal winners from the different classes at the Exhibition become elegible to enter for the Duke of Edinburgh Challenge Trophy in the following year. It was successful in this and the Trophy left the United Kingdom for the first time to go to Australia.

During the course of construction I have been given considerable help and encouragement by many people, too numerous to mention, but to whom I am, nevertheless, extremely grateful. It has also meant that I have met many interesting and distinguished people most of whom have become firm friends. It has in fact opened many doors into many places I would not otherwise have been. The whole project has been most rewarding in so many ways.

If there is something to be learned, perhaps it is that with increasing leisure time and earlier retirement it may encourage people to reach out into new fields. I was not a professional engineer and my working life was not closely allied to engineering. I believe this project has been of such absorbing interest because of being in a completely different field. I would encourage anyone who may suspect they have latent abilities or aptitudes to have a go. They might surprise themselves, as I have done.

Last but by no means least I am most grateful to Sir Laurence Hartnett for writing the foreword to this book. His distinguished career must have inspired many people. It included heading up the birth of the motor car manufacturing industry in Australia, as the Managing Director of General Motors, Australia, Director of Ordinance Production in Australia during World War 2, and playing a leading role in establishing the Australian aircraft industry in the post war period.

When Sir Laurence heard about this engine, he expressed an interest to see it running. When this was arranged the story unfolded of a very unique set of circumstances that make it most appropriate that he agreed to write the Foreword to this book.

Beginning with his memory of machining parts for the prototype engine at Vickers, seeing the first engine tested at the Vickers test house and later as a pilot in the R.N.A.S. he also witnessed the first Sopwith Snipes equipped with Bentley B.R.2. engines flying.

Lew Blackmore

BENTLEY B.R.2. Rotary Aero Engine. 235 H.P.

INTRODUCTION

The name Bentley is usually associated with the motor cars built during the latter half of the twenties and are one of the most sought after vintage cars in the world today. Production ceased in 1931 due to financial difficulties encountered by the firm which resulted in it being taken over by Rolls Royce who of course still use his name on one of their special line of motor cars. Rolls Royce did not utilise Bentley's engineering genius which was later to be associated with the design and development of the Lagonda and Armstrong Siddeley cars. Records and specifications of all the cars manufactured by Bentley are still in existence and a greater number of percentage of them are still on the road than any other motor car ever produced.

In 1913 W.O. Bentley and his brother had the English agency for the D.F.P. cars which they conducted from premises in London. From an early stage W.O., (as I will now refer to him), considered that competition in motor sports was not only highly enjoyable and challenging but was also convinced that the ensuing publicity was an important factor in promoting the sales of the D.F.P. cars. As a result of these activities to keep ahead of the opposition he gained considerable knowledge in the tuning of engines.

During this time he conceived the idea that the use of aluminium alloy pistons would greatly improve the performance. As aluminium alloy is approximately one third the weight of the then commonly used cast iron, its use would result in a great reduction in the reciprocating weights. This would in turn reduce the weight of the crankshaft and balance weights. Aluminium alloy also has very much superior heat conductivity properties, in the order of three to one. The use of the alloy resulted in a much more even distribution of heat, with the elimination of hot spots, and of course the heat was conducted away from the piston head at a much greater rate. This made possible the use of higher compression ratios which again improved performance. On his frequent visits to France in connection with his agency for the D.F.P. cars he designed and was able to get piston castings made from an alloy containing 88% aluminium and 12% copper which provided the properties required. These were tested out in his competition activities with great success and W.O. gained a reputation as an engine designer.

At the outbreak of World War 1, he was given a commission in the Royal Navy as a Technical Consultant. Initially he was posted to Gwynnes who were making the 130H.P. Clerget engine under licence from the Clerget factory in France. At the time these engines were being extensively used in France on the Western Front and were giving serious overheating problems which will be dealt with at a later stage. Visits to France to observe at first hand the problems which were causing so many casualties of both pilots and machines soon caused his inventive mind to work out solutions to the problems.

On his return to England he endeavoured to get Gwynnes to incorporate aluminium alloy pistons, which they were most reluctant to do. However some Clergets were fitted with the alloy pistons, which resulted in the expected improvement in performance and reliability. Generally however Gwynnes were under the influence of the French engineers and W.O. found himself in a difficult situation. Fortunately the powers-that-be at the Admiralty had faith in him and he was sent to Humbers. Apart from these problems the Clerget had about reached the end of its potential from a cubic capacity standpoint.

When W.O. was posted to Humbers he was given a very free rein to design a new and bigger engine which he proceeded to do in a very short time. This resulted in first the B.R.1 and shortly thereafter the B.R.2. This discussion will be confined to the B.R.2 as this is the subject of this publication. The B.R.2 was 24.9 litres while the Clerget was 16.28 litres. It must be understood that the rotary engines up to and including the B.R.2 had the cylinders disposed radially on the crankcase. The crankshaft was secured in mountings in the forward part of the airframe and the whole engine rotated about it. As there was very little reciprocating motion with respect to the crankpin, which was locked in the vertical position, there was no need for a massive counterweight for the array of connecting rods, big end and pistons. This meant that the weight of the engine as a whole was much reduced. Due to the, then, low forward speed of the aircraft, concerns were felt that the cylinders would not receive adequate cooling. Rotating the whole engine was thought necessary to assist this.

One thing which was common to all rotary engines was the method of lubrication. Due to the rotation of the whole engine it was clearly not possible to arrange any kind of lubricating oil circulating system. Because the fuel air mixture had to be introduced through the hollow crankshaft into the crankcase in which all the moving parts were situated, a special lubricant had to be used which would not be washed off. Castor oil was used as it was not compatible with petrol.

The oil was introduced by a metering pump mounted on the central support and driven from the main accessory drive gear. This pump supplied oil by a pipe to the oilways drilled in the crankshaft and forward to the maneton shaft. It was thus distributed to all the working parts right through to the cam gear at the front end. This was a total loss system, all surplus being thrown out which resulted in the aircraft and pilot being exposed to an oily mist which soon endowed them with an unpleasant appearance and smell.

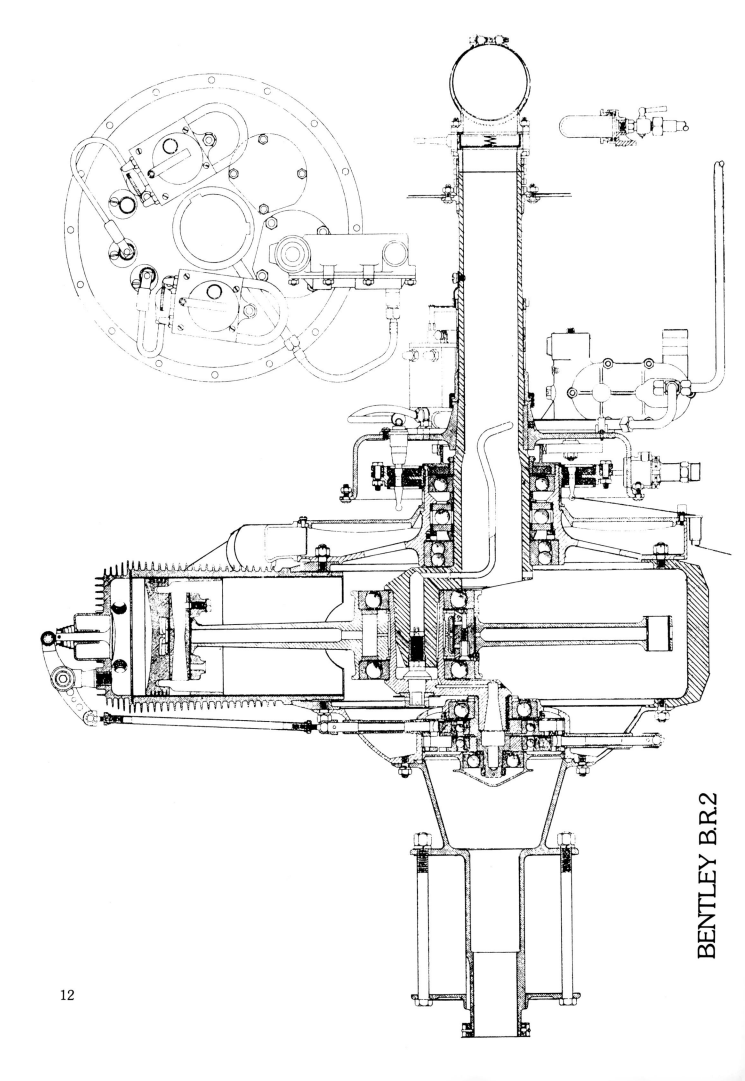

BENTLEY B.R.2

12

CLERGET AERO ENGINE 9 Z.
SINGLE IGNITION.

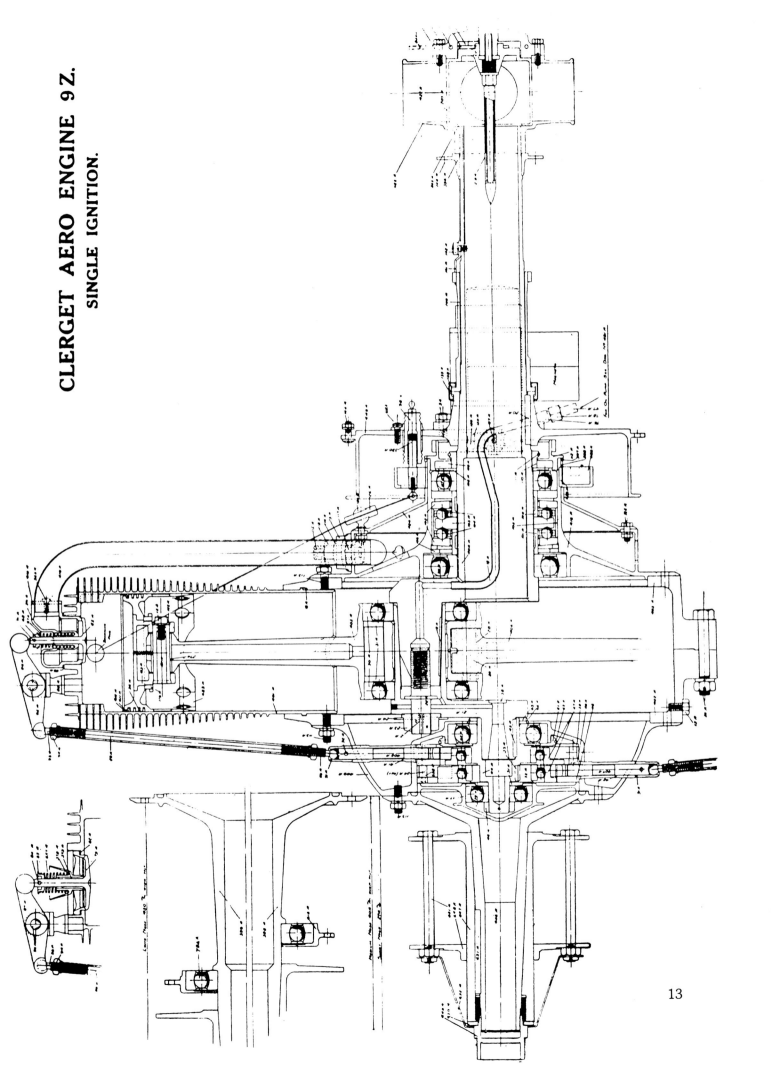

Basically the problem with all rotaries is that the leading side of the cylinder cools at a much greater rate than the trailing side. The cylinders of the Clerget were machined from steel to a very thin section with integral fins and cylinder heads to keep the weight within reasonable limits. Due to the very thin section and the poor heat conductivity of steel considerable distortion took place and the only way that the gases of combustion could be controlled was by the use of an 'L' shaped 'obturator' piston ring made of bronze which was situated at the top of the piston. The service life of these rings was about 15 hours, when the whole engine had to be dismantled for overhaul.

This was a major operation because the method of securing the cylinders in the crankcase was by a collar which was held by clamping between the halves of the split crankcase. Frequently the obturator rings broke which was closely followed by piston seizure and destruction of the engine. This frequently resulted in the loss of both the pilot and aircraft.

The Clerget engines were largely used in the Sopwith Camel which were extensively used in France and were a very successful fighter once mastered. The Camel got its name from the hump which enclosed the breeches of the twin machine guns which fired through the propellor. Warm air from the engine was passed over the breeches of the guns to prevent them freezing and being inoperative when required. All fighter aircraft fitted in this way had a gun interruptor gear to prevent damage to the propellor. The Camel was a very tricky aeroplane to handle and a lot of pilots were killed in training. Once they had mastered the peculiarities of the engine/airframe combination they were a very effective fighter, due to their extreme agility. These control problems were largely due to the gyroscopic forces of the rotating mass of the engine which resulted in a reaction at right angles to the control force applied, about which more later. W.O. was of course very familiar with the Clerget, having worked at Gwynnes. When given the opportunity to go to Humbers to design a new and more powerful engine it was to be a radical departure from the Clerget. He did however retain the valve operating gear which reflects on his practical approach to engineering problems. One could imagine that there was considerable pressure to put the new engine into production as early as possible and that he retained the cam gear as one feature that he felt was satisfactory.

Comparison between the two engines is interesting. Firstly of course is the use of the aluminium alloy, not only for the pistons but for the cylinder barrels, which had a shrunk in liner. This resulted in much better distribution of heat and permitted the use of normal cast iron piston rings and the discarding of the obturator ring. These changes increased greatly the time between overhauls and the reliability in service.

The Clerget cylinders as we have seen were machined from steel billets to a very thin section and had integral cylinder heads. All the valve gear therefore had to be assembled before the cylinders were installed. The crankcase was split circumferentially and the cylinders held between the halves by a collar machined on the skirt of the cylinder.

On the Clerget the induction pipe is at the rear of the cylinder. W.O. disposed the head on the B.R.2 so that the exhaust valve was on the leading side where it got maximum cooling. This configuration also placed the induction pipe at the trailing side, largely blanketed by the cylinder which reduced windage due to engine rotation.

The cylinder heads were separate from the cylinder barrels. They were machined from steel and were held, together with the cylinders, on to the one piece crankcase by four long bolts which were accommodated in grooves machined in the cooling fins the length of the cylinder barrels. These bolts were inserted from the inside of the crankcase and the head held in tapered holes. This meant that individual cylinders and heads could be removed without disturbing the whole engine, thus expediting any repairs or servicing that was required.

It will be seen that the valve rockers are of an unusual design, sloping down rather sharply from the pivot to the push rod socket. This was so that the engine could be accommodated within the limits of the cowling. It is interesting to note that the overall diameter of the B.R.2 is only three inches greater than the Clerget. This is remarkable when one considers that the Clerget developed 135 H.P. and the B.R.2, 235 H.P.

Comparison between the two engines is interesting:

	B.R.2	Clerget
Capacity Litres	24.9	16.28
Weight Lbs.	475	400
Compression ratio	5.3	4.36
Horse Power	235	135
Power/weight ratio Lbs./H.P.	2.00	3.28

It is remarkable that W.O. was able to increase the cubic capacity of the engine to such an extent that it is only 3" larger in outside diameter than the Clerget. The increase of weight was so well controlled that the power/weight ratio drops from 3.28 to 2.00. What the figures do not show is the great increase in reliability achieved from the improved heat distribution resulting from the use of aluminium alloys.

The Bentley B.R.2 was the last of the rotaries for several reasons. The increasing forward speed of the aircraft ensured the passage of an adequate mass of cooling air without the need for the whole engine to rotate. The main reason however was probably the magnitude of the gyroscopic forces in the rotating mass of the engine, which, with increasing engine weight, caused serious aircraft control problems. Lifting the tail in the early stages of the take-off run produced precessional forces at right angles which tended to make the aircraft veer sharply to the left. This was called the gyroscopic 'kick' by the pilots and unless positive and early corrective action was taken with the rudder, disaster would ensue. The rudder and fin area of course needed to be adequate to provide the necessary correction. Again when the nose was raised as flying speed was attained, the 'kick' would be in the opposite direction which resulted in many spectacular turns to the right immediately on take-off. This was particularly dangerous as, at this stage, the air speed had not built up to the point where anything but the gentlest turn could be undertaken without an aerodynamic stall resulting.

Turns in either direction in the air resulted in strong nose up or nose down forces which had to be contended with and which formed an important consideration in aircraft handling and fighter tactics. The rotary engined aircraft could turn very tightly to the right and much less so to the left. As the Germans were using in-line engines which were not subjected to these forces they were sometimes able to get on a favourable side for them to fire a prolonged burst.

The Sopwith Camels experienced severe control problems with the engines up to 135 H.P. then being used. When a heavier and much more powerful engine was proposed it was clear that an aeroplane had to be designed to handle these increasing control problems. The Sopwith Snipe was the result of this and was a development from the Camel which had been so successful but lacked the power that was being increasingly requested to maintain superiority in the air over France. The Snipe was an update in many ways and of course had greatly increased control surface area. The cowling enclosing the breeches of the twin machine guns appeared as a more integral part of the aeroplane. One thing of note in both these aircraft is the extremely short length of fuselage in which the weight is concentrated which contributed to their very quick control response to any control movement.

The first Sopwith Snipe flew with a B.R.2 engine in October 1917, although one had been test flown with the 150 H.P. B.R.1 engine a month earlier. It was immediately apparent that it was going to be a very effective replacement for the Camel.

It is interesting to note that from the time of its first flight in September 1917 orders totaled 5,333 up to the end of November 1918, when hostilities ended. 2,103 of these were delivered up to this time when the outstanding orders for 3,230 were cancelled.

A Sopwith 'Snipe' fighter with a Bentley B.R.2 engine.

There are documented records of the Snipe in action, including one dogfight during which Major Barker shot down three enemy in an heroic action, during which he was wounded three times. He was awarded the last Victoria Cross of the war.

The Snipe proved itself to be the best fighter to see action during the war. It subsequently saw considerable service in other areas, notably Russia and the Middle East. It was used extensively in the post war period in the R.A.F. for training up to 1926 when it was declared obsolete, with the arrival of more up to date aircraft.

It was certainly used extensively in the 1920s. The late Air Commodore Allen Wheeler devotes a chapter to the Snipe in his book, 'Flying Between the Wars', which makes very interesting reading. He deals with its flying characteristics and writes about its ability to fly inverted.

As will be seen from the Air Ministry Handbook description, an air pump was fitted to the central support and driven from the accessory drive gear. This was to pressurise the fuel system and provide an adequate supply of fuel to the engine. Some arrangement was obviously made to ensure an uninterrupted supply of fuel from the tank to permit a continuity of supply, for periods while in the inverted position.

As the 'Bloctube' carburettor had no float chamber it was the forerunner to the fuel injection system fitted to aircraft petrol engines later it was quite feasible for it to operate in any position provided the supply of fuel was maintained.

Starting up a B.R.2 in a Sopwith Snipe with the aid of a 'Hucks' starter.

BUILDING THE QUARTER SCALE MODEL

When it was decided to build a model of the Bentley B.R.2 the next question to be settled was the scale that was to be used. One quarter full size was selected for the following reasons. It would be large enough to make a practical working model, not too unwieldy to transport around, while remaining within the capacity of the available workshop equipment.

The engine has been most reliable, easy to start on all occasions and runs very smoothly. The great interest it has aroused probably results from a recapture of the nostalgia for the early days of aviation as it was in the early twenties. People could still identify with the human aspects of flying when individual skill, courage and the spirit of adventure were the order of the day and pilots really did literally fly by the seat of their pants, before the black boxes and Jumbos and supersonic flight when those qualities were submerged in the technical development.

It has surprised me that so many people are quite astounded that the whole engine rotates and that it is the crankshaft that is secured to the engine mountings. The odour of burning castor oil and the blue smoke which is dispersed adds to its authenticity.

When the engine was completed it was entered in the 1981 Model Engineer Exhibition at Wembley, London, where it was awarded a Gold Medal in the internal combustion engine class. Professor Chaddock demonstrated it running before a great number of people at various venues in the U.K.

Winning the Gold Medal made it eligible to compete for the Duke of Edinburgh Challenge Trophy at the Exhibition the following year. This Trophy is awarded to the overall winner of all the classes at the previous Exhibition and it was successful in winning. This was the first time that the Duke of Edinburgh Award had been won outside the United Kingdom. Another first was established when it was removed from the special display stand and transferred to the stand of the Society of Model & Experimental Engineers so that it could be given demonstration runs at regular intervals throughout the duration of the Exhibition.

The publishers of the 'Model Engineer' magazine had commissioned me to write a full description of the construction of this engine, not only because of its success and the interest that it had attracted but because also it was an unusual model. It was of interest because the methods used in its construction are somewhat more complex than are used in the more usual model engineering project. Model and Allied Publications also wished to reproduce the full set of working drawings of it for their plans service.

The constructional article ran in serial form in the 'Model Engineer' beginning in the issue which came out the same week in which it won the Duke of Edinburgh Award. The interest in the B.R.2 and the publication of the plans and serial article has prompted several people to build copies. One built in England by Mr. Woolfall won a gold medal at the 1984 Exhibition and one built by Mr. Reg Wood of Sydney, Australia, won a gold medal at the 1985 Exhibition. Mr. Wood's engine was also run on the S.M.E.E. stand throughout the Exhibition by Professor Chaddock. It embodied some detail improvements, the most noticeable of which is the use of the correct volute valve springs made from flat spring steel strip. I am grateful to Mr. Wood for his cooperation in allowing me to publish some of his variations such as details of making the valve springs and the use of commercial ball races. He used 32 D.P. gears for the accessory drive. These were available commercially and did not involve any serious alteration to the original design. A small increase in the diameter of the rear support is the only visible change. He was able to make a built-up main gear incorporating an 'O' ring seal and drawing of this variation is included.

The widespread interest that has been displayed together with the success of the engine, encouraged consideration being given to publishing the information, drawings and photographs under one cover, incorporating at the same time corrections of errors that had occurred during publication of the serial article. Professor Chaddock made a great contribution in checking and co-ordinating the material with the 'Model Engineer' and published these in a special article in the M.E. at the conclusion of the serial. The design given here incorporates these, together with some alternate methods of construction, including the separate exhaust valve cage, valve springs and use of commercial ball races on the crankshaft.

It will be assumed that the prospective builder is familiar with normal heat treatment processes for the metals to be used both in the model and the tools used in its production. These consist of hardening and tempering silver steel and case hardening.

The drawings have been amended to take the commercial bearings specified and also the 32 D.P. gears. The section on making the accessory drive gears has also been amended so this now applies to 32 D.P. instead of 36 D.P.

At least two other B.R.2s are being built in Australia. These engines have been made from my original drawings and the description, serialised in the 'Model Engineer'. There is no necessity to use high

All photographs in this section of the book are of the one quarter full size model.

specification materials. It must be remembered that although it is to one quarter scale and all sections are reduced in this proportion, the cubic capacity and potential power output is only one sixty-fourth of this. There is no danger therefore that problems will occur so far as strength of materials is concerned. This also applies with cooling as the surface area within the cylinder is one sixteenth.

When one is building a replica it is important to adhere to the original so far as possible and this applies to the materials and finish of the original. One builder has used inlet pipe fittings fabricated by silver soldering copper elbows plated in a satin chrome finish. These look very well but it is not possible to accurately reproduce the shape in this way and of course is a departure from the aluminium alloy used in the original. With the availability of lost wax casting which will reproduce the parts to perfection, I would recommend this.

Lubrication is by a total loss system supplied by a worm-driven oscillating plunger pump of 1/8" bore x 5/32" stroke running at 1/16 engine speed. The internal worm gear is 36 to 1. Both the oil pump and the contact breaker are driven at two and a quarter times engine speed. The oil intake for the pump is of large diameter to ensure that there is no restriction of supply under extreme cold conditions. A branch pipe is taken from the oil pump delivery to the 'pulsometer' which provides a visual indication in the glass that the pump is working.

Due to the fact that the fuel/air mixture is ingested through the hollow crankshaft and comes into contact with the internal moving parts of the engine, a mineral oil cannot be used or it would be washed off. A castor oil such as Castrol R30 is therefore used for lubrication and straight petrol with no additives which would carry the castor oil out.

The model B.R.2 from the rear.

LEADING PARTICULARS OF THE ONE QUARTER SCALE MODEL B.R.2.

Type of engine	Rotary 9 cylinder
Swept vol. per cylinder	38.48 cc or 2.34 cu.in.
Swept volume - total	347.00 cc or 21.17 cu.in.
Bore	33mm
Stroke	45mm
Compression ratio	5.6 to 1
Direction of rotation	Right hand tractor clockwise from rear.
Lubrication system	Total loss from worm driven oscillating plunger pump 1/8" bore 5/32" stroke running at 1/16 engine speed.
Carburettor	Bloctube with slide throttle and fuel metering needle.
Ignition	Dual ignition system. Coil energised by a contact breaker giving two sparks per revolution running at two and a quarter x engine speed.
Spark timing	20 deg. before top centre.
Exhaust tappets	Front row.
Inlet tappets	Rear row.

No detailed drawings could be found of the engine. The basis for the design was taken from the Air Ministry Handbook. The main sectioned drawing from this was used as a design layout, using the known bore and stroke of the engine. Considerable work was required to reconstruct details of the design. Machining procedures had then to be worked out. Construction of numerous machining fixtures, jigs and tools was required. Many of the parts were required in multiples. Apart from speeding up production the procedures adopted ensured the uniformity of the parts, essential to true running and good balance.

GENERAL CONSTRUCTIONAL DETAILS

The following constructional details assume that anyone undertaking building a B.R.2 will be experienced in small engineering procedures and have an adequately equipped workshop. For this reason the details of fixtures, jigs, tools and machining procedures have been confined to those of a relatively specialised nature. They do not cover production of components which only require obvious and commonly used practices.

The use of two systems of measurement was brought about partly by the machine tools used, some of which were calibrated in metric units and others in imperial. It was also more convenient to develop the engine design using the metric system. However drill sizes and screw threads in imperial measurements and B.A. were adopted and some mixing of the two systems was inevitable. One gets quite used to working in both systems so no great problems arise.

The machine tools required are quite obviously a well equipped lathe with collets, a vertical milling machine; associated equipment includes a worm-driven rotary table capable of being mounted vertically as well as on its base. Dividing equipment must be available and the following divisions are required:

54	Main accessory drive gear.
36-18-9	Crankcase items. Valve internal gears.
24	Magneto and oil pump gears.
16	Cam gears.
14	Nose piece to cambox mounting flange.

Numerous special milling cutters and tools will be required so the expertise and equipment for producing these and hardening and tempering them is required. All cutters must be of the type which are securely held axially in the chuck. A lot of machining procedures rely on reference to the micrometer indexes and constant regard must be had for the backlash in the lead screws. The machine tools each require to be equipped with cutting fluid pumps. Most of the machining is in steel or aluminium alloy both of which require a constant flow as a necessity to keep the tool cool, wash away chips as they are formed and to ensure a good finish 'off the tool'.

All machining operations have been planned in a logical sequence and operations broken down to where a complete run can be done on all units before going on to the next stage. The fixtures and jigs have been designed so that components may be returned to them and secured accurately for subsequent operations. They are in some cases so designed that they may be transferred from one machine to the other. Drilling jigs and bushes should be case-hardened and drill guide holes should be at least 1 x D in length. Once the initial set-up is made operations on subsequent items are in many cases made by reference to micrometer indexes on the machine's feed screws. A trial component is run through and a complete log of all micrometer

19

KEY

1. Crankcase
2. Cam box
3. Nose piece
4. Propellor flange
5. Thrust box
6. Thrust box cover
7. Front bearing carrier
8. Bearing retainer
9. Centre support
10. Maneton shaft
11. Crankshaft
12. Main gear
13. Crankshaft sleeve nut
14. Crankshaft locknut
15. Cylinder head
16. Cylinder
17. Induction pipe
18. Push-rod
19. Rocker
20. Valve
21. Rocker bracket
22. Valve spring
23. Ring gears
24. Exhaust eccentric
25. Eccentric shaft
26. Cam gears
27. Timing diagram
28. Eccentric setting
29. Keyway location
30. Master and slave rods
31. Thrust bridge assembly
32. Piston
33. Gudgeon pin
34. Wrist-pin
35. Tappets.

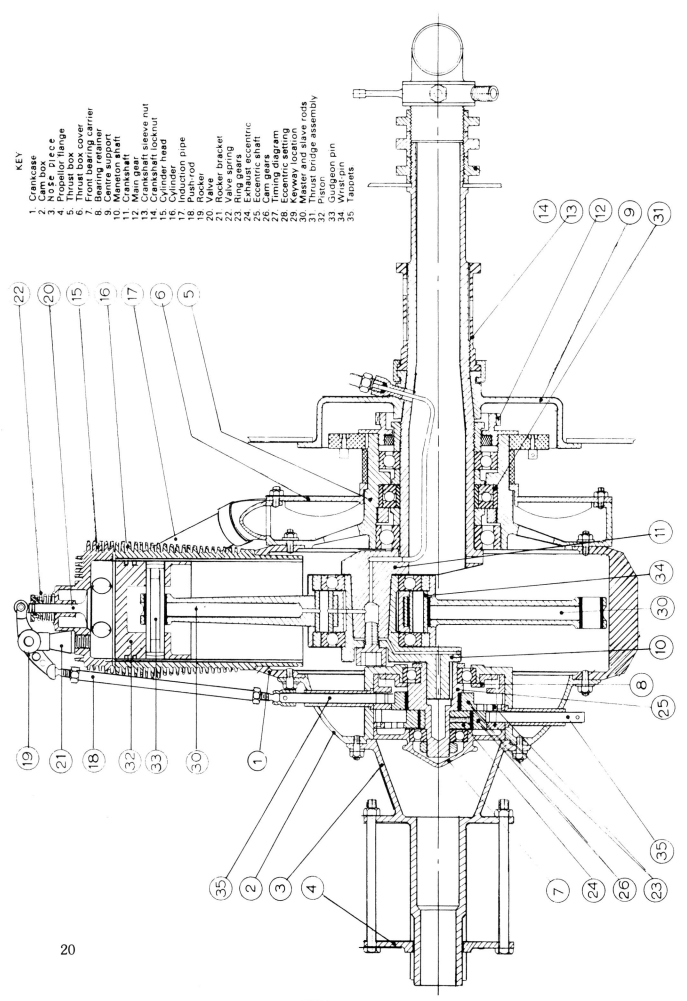

BENTLEY B.R.2. Model Rotary Aero Engine

readings is made. This also gives the opportunity to try out all the special jigs and tools and if necessary make any alterations before the production run is put through. One has to give considerable thought to the sequence of operations having particular regard to and allowing for backlash in the feed screws and feed related to the direction of rotation of the cutter. One has to be sure that the positioning and feed in any cut must be contrary to the rotation of the cutter to avoid any disastrous snatching.

The following description is in some cases necessarily rather involved. The object is to present the approach used to the procedures involved. This will become much clearer when the fixtures, jigs and tools are made and set up with a blank on the machine. It is well worthwhile to regard, at least, the first one off as a trial piece to establish the equipment, tooling and the system. Once this is done it will be found that the 'learning curve' rapidly rises and the output progressively improves. It is advisable to make extra components, particularly the major ones, while a run is being done in case of some defects in subsequent operations.

Working drawings cover the dimensional sizes for the component parts and the various fixtures, jigs and cutters. These are referred to in the text as 'drawings' and numbered.

Machining procedures and explanatory drawings are not necessarily to scale and are referred to in the text as 'diagrams' and numbered.

The special tools and milling cutters required can be made of silver steel which will do good work at a reasonable rate provided they are kept well supplied with a continuous flow of cutting fluid.

Ball bearings for the original engine were made. However commercial bearings are now available and are detailed in the accompanying drawing, which gives details of the bearing layout in the engine. The Thrust bearing will have to be made of suitable steel and hardened or case hardened. 1/8" balls are used.

The quarter full size model Bentley B.R.2.

THE CRANKCASE

THE CRANKCASE ASSEMBLY consists of three main parts which form the basic structure of the engine. Before they can be machined the two fixtures required for doing this must be made.

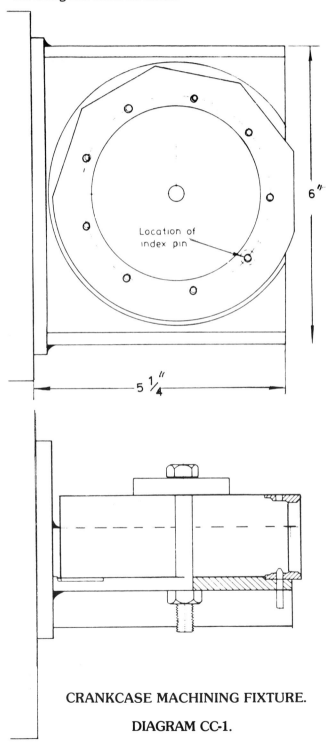

CRANKCASE MACHINING FIXTURE.

DIAGRAM CC-1.

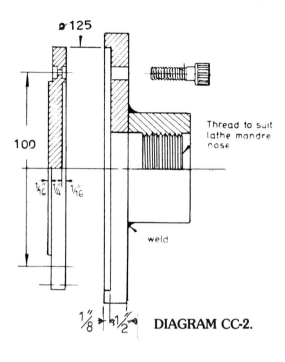

DIAGRAM CC-2.

MACHINING FIXTURES FOR THE CRANKCASE

The box angle plate fixture is used to face and bore the nine cylinder barrel seatings around the circumference of the crankcase. *Diagram CC-1.*

It is fabricated and welded from quarter inch thick steel plate. The recess and locating spigot is machined while it is clamped flat on to the face plate. When the fixture is bolted on to the face plate on its base for machining the cylinder seatings, the crankcase must be checked and packing used if necessary to set it at right angles to the face-plate.

The index pin hole can be located through one of the untapped holes in the side of the crankcase, making sure the crankcase is correctly disposed with respect to the whole layout.

It is vital that the spigots on the cambox, thrustbox and the adaptor plate all fit their mating recesses closely. All diameters must be held accurately to 90mm. The parts must be a light push fit.

The other fixture required for machining the crankcase components consists of a chuck back plate with an annular recess 1/8" depth to locate the adaptor plate accurately either way so that it can be reversed to accept either a male or female location as required. The adaptor plate must fit this recess accurately. The two are held together by three screws at intermediate positions but on the same 100mm pitch circle diameter as the previously drilled row. *Diagram CC-2.*

The first function of this fixture is to hold the crankcase while the bevels are machined on each side. It is also used to accurately locate and hold, in turn, the cambox and the thrustbox to carry out the final machining operations on them.

It is an advantage if the recess in the chucking plate is machined to fit the adaptor plate after the three main crankcase components are finished up to the stage where they can all in turn be completed without disturbing the chucking plate on the lathe.

MACHINING THE CRANKCASE Part No.1.

Face off one side of a 2" length of 6" diameter free cutting steel bar. Reverse in the chuck and bore through 90 mm diameter to fit the adaptor spigot. Bore out the inside as shown on the drawings. Leave a few thou. to true up the front face when it is reversed on the adaptor plate.

Remove from the chuck and drill a circular row of 18 holes on a pitch circle diameter of 100mm using the adaptor plate as a jig. The holes in the adaptor plate will be clearance size for 6BA. Nine of the holes therefore must be initially spotted through with a clearance size

drill. Then drill through with a tapping size drill and tap 6BA to accept screws entering from the back of the adaptor plate to carry out the machining. These threads are later drilled out to 6BA clearing size.

Secure the partly finished crankcase to the adaptor plate set to run true in the lathe. Face off to finish size and jig drill, repeating the steps performed on the first side making sure that the holes are perfectly aligned with the circular row of holes drilled in the first side.

Transfer the crankcase to the machining box. Locate by inserting a pin through one of the untapped holes in the crankcase. Clamp down with the 3/8" bolt and the bridging piece. The indexing pin must be positioned so that the cylinder seating centres line up with one of the holes so that the studs which later secure the cam and thrust box alternately lie on the cylinder centre line and the mid point between the cylinders.

Face and bore, in turn, each of the nine cylinder barrel seating holes making sure that they are all faced at the correct radius from the centre. One way to ensure all are uniform is to rough bore them out in turn. Then set the boring tool to cut to the finished diameter and

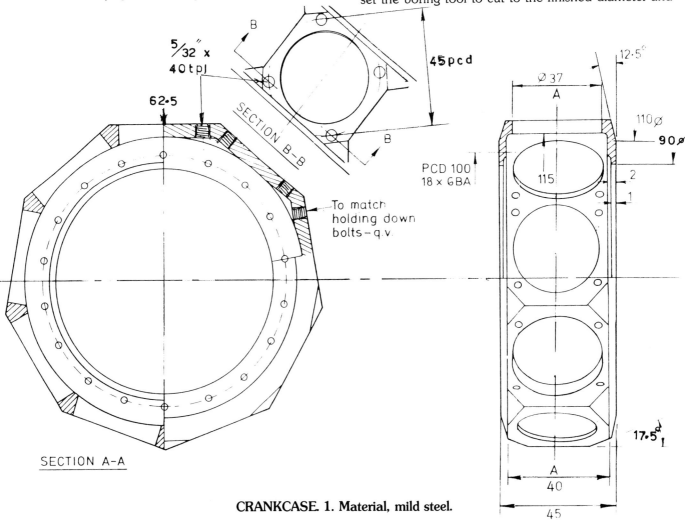

CRANKCASE. 1. Material, mild steel.

SECTION A-A

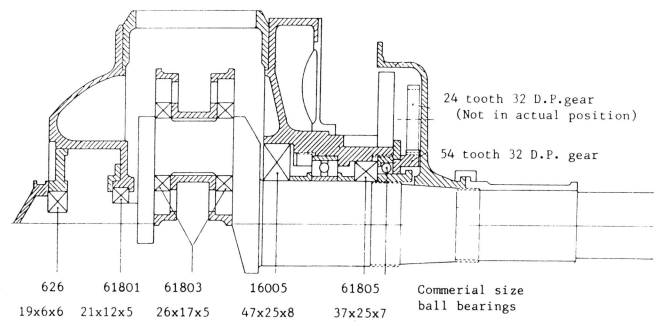

					24 tooth 32 D.P. gear
					(Not in actual position)
					54 tooth 32 D.P. gear

626	61801	61803	16005	61805	Commerial size
19x6x6	21x12x5	26x17x5	47x25x8	37x25x7	ball bearings

Diagram showing use of commercial ball bearings.

repeat all the finishing cuts on all nine bores without disturbing the tool setting, indexing round into each position. The facing can be done in the same way. Finish each one in turn without disturbing the tool setting and with the saddle locked to ensure that it does not move.

When the seatings have all been completed the machining box may be removed from the face plate, and stood on its base to hold the crankcase in position to drill the tapping size holes for the 5/32" x 40 tpi. cylinder holding down studs, using the special jig *Diagram CC-5 (page 41)*. While it is set up tap the 5/32" x 40 threads using a tapping guide held in the drill chuck. It is absolutely vital that these are truly vertical by making use of a guide.

Mount on the *adaptor plate CC-2*, again and finish the two bevels on the front and rear faces of the crankcase. The cylinder numbering can now be stamped on the inner bevel below each cylinder seating. It will be noted that the numbering goes from zero to 8. The figure 9 is not used so as to avoid any possibility of confusion with the figure 6. As these numbers are very visible they must be stamped accurately and to be sure of getting them right it is worth while making up a simple jig to guide the punch.

THE THRUST BOX, Part No. 5 is bolted to the rear of the crankcase.

An aluminium alloy cover plate is bolted on to its rear face by 36 10BA screws, and covers the annular recess in the rear of the thrust box, forming the distribution chamber. The fuel/air mixture enters through the nine holes in the main web and is drawn out through the radial ports in the outer diameter into the induction pipes.

Inside the thrust box are located the two main ball bearings and the thrust bearing. The inner bore of the cover plate is held in place by a spacer which in the full size engine is a steel sleeve with lightening holes. In the quarter scale model and because the H.T. voltage cannot be scaled this sleeve is made of insulating material to prevent sparking over to earth from the distributor connections. Behind the spacer the insulator distributor disc is clamped by the flange on the front of the main 54 tooth accessory drive gear. This gear screws into the female thread in the rear of the thrust box. The rear oil seal is incorporated in the centre portion of the gear. The distributor disc is held from rotating by a key.

The crankcase machining fixture.

MACHINING THE THRUST BOX

Chuck a piece of 5" diameter free cutting mild steel and remove all surplus material, leaving the rear portion turned to 60mm diameter. Reverse in the chuck by the rough turned spigot and finish turn to 117mm outside diameter. Complete all the machining on the front face. Finish the bore for the front main bearing and the thrust race and screw cut the 42mm diameter by 40 tpi. thread for the thrust race retainer. Drill the circular row of 18 holes on a pitch circle of 100mm using the adaptor plate as a drilling jig. Tap 9 of these holes 6BA. Mount on the adaptor plate. *It will be noted that when the thrust box is mated to the back of the crankcase its overall diameter is greater than that of its mating face on the crankcase.*

Finish machining the rear of the thrust box. Bore out for the rear bearing and screwcut the left hand internal thread 41mm x 40 tpi. for the main gear to screw into.

Index and drill the 9 x half inch holes in the main web for lightening and communication between the main crankcase and the distribution box, so that the fuel/air mixture can get through. Drill and tap the 36 holes 10BA for the screws which secure the alloy cover plate for the distribution box.

An exploded view of the crankcase components.

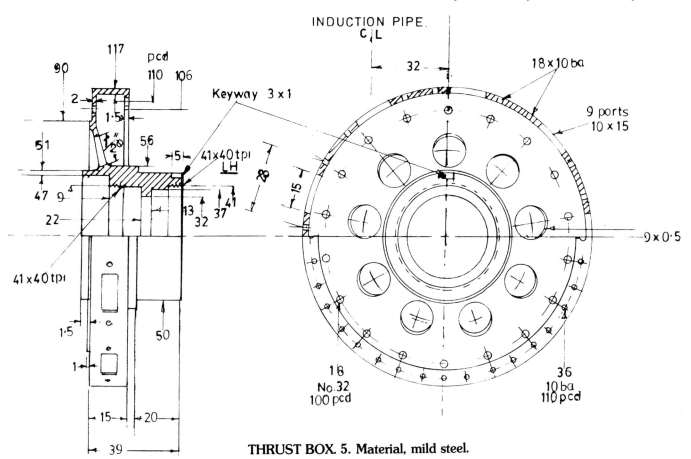

THRUST BOX. 5. Material, mild steel.

26

The whole assembly should now be set up in the milling machine so that it can be indexed around for machining the nine rectangular apertures on the outer diameter for the outlets to the induction pipes. The 18 holes for the induction pipe fitting, holding studs and screws, should be drilled at this time. The keyway for the distributor disc key can be cut while it is set up.

THE CAM GEAR BOX is bolted to the front of the crankcase by 18 studs. This carries the 18 radially disposed tappet guides in two rows. The rear row are the inlet tappets and the front row the exhaust tappets. Inside the cam case the internally toothed cam gear rings are keyed and held in place by the nose piece and located by a key. This nose piece is made in one with the propeller shaft and bolts on to the front of the cam box by 14 studs. The front propeller flange is splined to the propeller shaft and clamps the propeller on to the rear propeller flange by 8 bolts.

The thrust box.

CAM BOX. 2. Material, mild steel.

MACHINING THE CAM GEAR BOX

Chuck a piece of free machining mild steel 4" diameter and finish the rear face, leaving the area shown shaded on diagram CC-4 until after the holes for the tappet guides holes are drilled. Index and drill 18 holes in the flange on 100mm pcd. Nine of these must be tapping size of 6BA to take the screws which secure the blank to the machining adaptor. While drilling on the pitch circle the 36 intermediate lightening holes should be drilled through the flange 5/32" diameter. Mount on the adaptor, secured to the chucking plate on the lathe.

Finish machining the cam case bore and front face, again leaving the shaded area until the tappet guide holes are drilled. Set up on the milling machine so that it can be indexed round to drill the two rows of nine radial holes which take the tappet guides. While it is set up, the counter bores for the heads of the tappet guides can be made with the special reverse counterbore as shown in the accompanying drawing and photograph. The upward travel must be limited by a stop so that they are all counterbored to the correct depth.

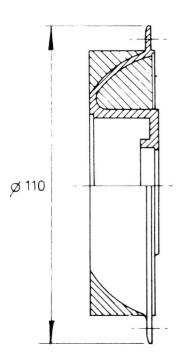

Diagram CC 4.

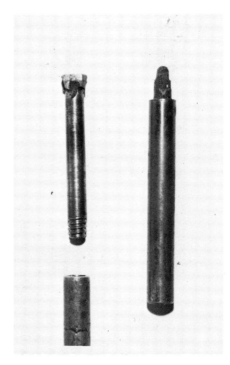

Tappet guide seating spotfacer.
Tappet ball seat cutter.

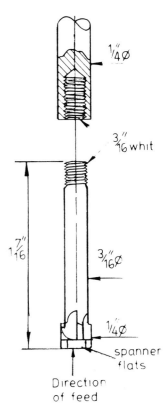

Direction of feed

Transfer to the lathe and finish turn the domed face of the cambox, taking care to get the correct profile. Drill and tap for the 14 x 6BA holes on the front face on a 55mm pcd. to mate with the propeller shaft flange. The numbering can be done on the cam box as described earlier.

Cam box complete.

THE NOSEPIECE is turned from steel bar. The rear portion, aft of the propeller flange is first dealt with. The 14 clearance holes for the 6BA studs are drilled. While it is set up it is used for a chucking piece for the cambox for the final operation of removing the portion, shaded in the diagram from the back. While it is set up the 4 x 10 BA bearing retainer screw holes can be indexed, drilled and tapped.

A chucking piece is now required to mate with the rear face of the Nose Piece for carrying out the rest of the machining forward of the propeller flange. This includes the propeller shaft and the splines. With the nose piece set up in the lathe the front end is turned and the bolt holes for the propeller bolts and the lightening holes are indexed and drilled as specified.

A specially made milling cutter is used to cut the splines. The same cutter is used to mill a drift, required to finish the female splines in the front propeller flange.

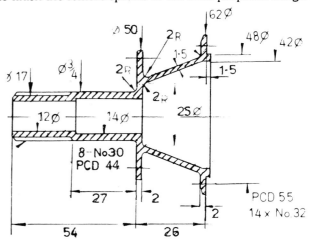

NOSEPIECE. Material, mild steel.

Propellor shaft spline cutter and drift.

THE FRONT PROPELLER FLANGE

This is made from quarter inch steel plate. The central hole is drilled to the root diameter of the spline. The splines are roughed out by hand and finally cleaned out with the drift. Some light hand finishing will be required to obtain a good fit with the mating splines on the shaft. The blank can then be pressed on to a true running spigot and finished all over. The propeller bolt holes and the lightening holes can then be indexed and drilled, making sure that the bolt holes will be in alignment with the holes on the Nosepiece when the splines are engaged.

FRONT BEARING CARRIER

This is machined to the drawing to fit the recess for it in the front of the cam box. It is held in place by the Nosepiece. It carries the front ball bearing and is located by a keyway which engages the front end of the key which aligns the cam gear rings. These are in turn held in together with the spacer by the front bearing carrier.

THRUST BOX COVER

Face one side of the aluminium alloy blank and then reverse in the chuck. Turn the front face leaving a spigot to mate with the rear of the thrust box. Profile the radius on the front face to form the tops of the stiffening webs. These have to be milled out by transferring to the milling machine. Index and drill the 36 clearing size holes for the 10BA securing screws. The cover plate can now be temporarily attached to the thrust box, which, in turn is set up on the machining fixture CC-2. The rear face of the cover can now be finished.

This completes the work on the component parts of the crankcase.

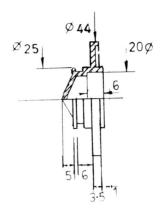

FRONT BEARING CARRIER. 7.
Material, mild steel.
material b m s

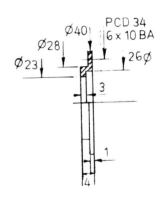

BEARING RETAINER. 8.
Material, mild steel.

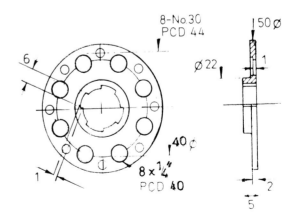

PROPELLER FLANGE Material, mild steel.

29

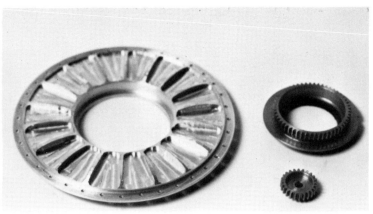

The thrust box cover plate, and accessory drive gears.

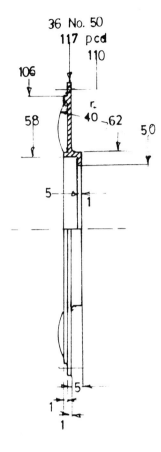

THRUST BOX COVER,

Material Alum. alloy.

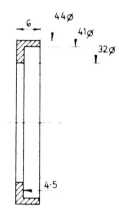

SPACING RING 23, Material, mild steel.

THE CRANKSHAFT

THE CRANKSHAFT
is built up of three sections.

THE MAIN CRANKSHAFT Part No.11

THE SHORT CRANK OR MANETON Part No.10

THE ECCENTRIC SHAFT Part No.25

THE CRANKSHAFT is machined from high tensile steel. If this is from a round section it is advisable to use a bar the full diameter to avoid distortion. Crankpin and crankshaft centres are marked out on each end. Mount between centres and rough turn to 1mm over size leaving both centres in the rear end. Mount between centres and turn and finish the crank pin. Taper the outside of the crank pin to fit accurately the taper inside the maneton shaft crank pin, checking the fit with bearing blue. Drill the oil holes to depth and cut the keyway and the oil groove to convey oil to the maneton shaft. After all the machining is done on the crank pin the lug on the rear end of the crankshaft which has the rear crank pin centre in it can be cut off.

Chuck the crankshaft in the four jaw chuck. Adjust so that it runs true when checked with a dial test indicator.

Centre and bore out to depth 11/16" diameter and then 9/16" as shown on the drawing, tapering the transition. At this stage do not bore right through as the rear centre for the crankshaft is required for further operations.

Finish the bevel on the rear of the main crank and while mounted in the chuck assemble the maneton shaft on to the main shaft with the key installed and lock it in with the maneton screw.

Finish the short stub shaft on the front of the maneton shaft to fit the bore of the Cam Gear shaft and cut the 1 m.m. keyway then finish the crank web.

Chuck a 3/4" shaft for a mandrel. Turn the projecting part to a push fit in the hole bored in the crankshaft. Drill and tap a cross hole for a driving peg 1/4" Whitworth. Screw in a short length of screwed rod to bear on the side of the crank pin to take the drive. The crank pin should be protected from damage. Push the crankshaft on to the mandrel up to the shoulder and bring up the rear centre to the back end centre in the crankshaft.

Turn and finish all diameters and the 6 degrees included angle taper to engage the central support. Cut the three 40 tpi. threads as shown on the drawing. While mounted on the mandrel the crankshaft can be drilled right through from the rear end to meet the previously drilled hole. End mill the main locating key way on the tapered portion of the shaft. This key handles the full torque loading of the engine, with its mounting and must be a good fit. It must align with the crankpin. Mill the oil distribution groove from the rear crank web along the top of the shaft, which feeds oil to the thrust box bearings. Drill all the remaining oil passages as shown on the drawings.

The crankshaft assembly.

CRANKSHAFT.

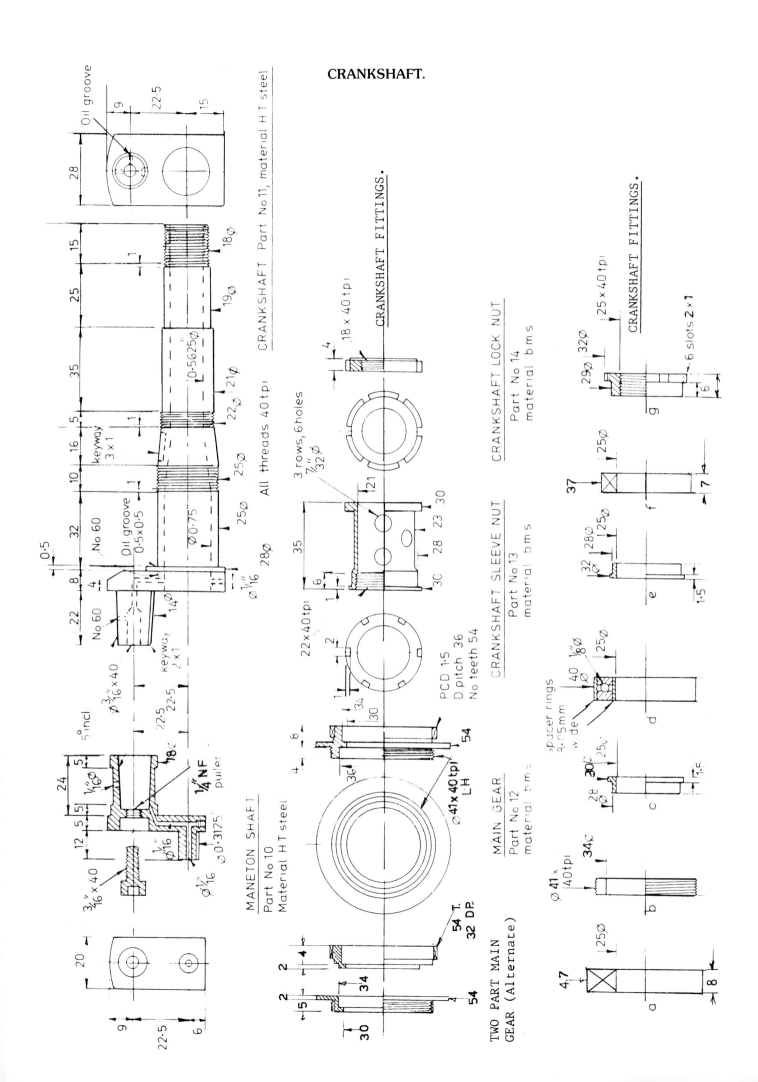

Oil groove

28 9 22.5 15

CRANKSHAFT Part No 11, material HT steel

CRANKSHAFT FITTINGS.

18 × 40 tpi

15 25 35 5 16 10 32 8 22

1 18∅ 19∅ 0·5625∅ 21∅ 22∅ 25∅ 25∅ 28∅

keyway 3 × 1

No 60
Oil groove 0·5 × 0·5
No 60

∅0·75 ∅1/16" 28∅

All threads 40 tpi

0·5

MANETON SHAFT
Part No 10
Material HT steel

5° incl
∅3/16" × 40

22.5 22.5

keyway 2 × 1

24 5 5 12 5 5

∅1/16 1/4" NF puller

1/2"16∅ 18∅

∅0·3125

3/16" × 40

∅1/16

20 9 22.5 6

3 rows, 6 holes
7/32"∅

21

28 23 30
30

35 6 1
22 × 40 tpi

2
30 34

8
36

54

∅41 × 40 tpi LH

PCD 1·5
D pitch 36
No teeth 54

54 T.
32 DP.

2 4
2 5
30 34
54

TWO PART MAIN
GEAR (Alternate)

MAIN GEAR
Part No 12
material bms

CRANKSHAFT FITTINGS.

CRANKSHAFT LOCK NUT
Part No 14
material bms

25 × 40 tpi

29∅ 32∅

6 slots 2 × 1

6

g

CRANKSHAFT SLEEVE NUT
Part No 13
material bms

37 25∅
7
f

32 28∅ 25∅
1.5
e

spacer rings 3·05 mm wide
40 1/8"∅ 25∅
d

28 30∅ 25∅
1.5
c

∅41 × 40 tpi 34∅
b

4.7 25∅
8
a

The tapered joint between Parts numbered 10 and 11 is located by a long key and pulled together by the maneton screw. The eccentric shaft 25 is a push fit on the front of the maneton shaft and is located by a keyway as explained in the Valve Gear section.

The rear end of the crankshaft assembly is rigidly mounted in its supports with the crankpin in the vertical position. The petrol/air mixture is drawn from the carburettor through the hollow centre of the shaft into the crankcase. The main oil supply pipe is located inside the crankshaft, conveying oil from the central support to the drillings in the crankshaft. A duct drilled down the centre of the front crank web supplies oil for the lubrication of the cam gear assembly.

There are four main ball bearings on the Crankshaft. Two support the Thrust box, and two the Cam Gear box. A ball thrust bearing is fitted in the Thrust box between the two main bearings.

THE MANETON Part No. 10 forms the outer part of the crankpin which carries the ball races for the big end. The two parts of the crankshaft are forcibly drawn together by the socket headed maneton screw. In order to separate this joint the hole through which the maneton screw passes is tapped one quarter inch x N.F. A temporary bolt can be screwed into this, bearing on the end of the inner crank pin, forcing it out. First machine the Maneton shaft from H.T. steel. Mount the blank eccentrically in the four jaw chuck. Turn the crank pin to fit the big end ball bearings. Bore and taper to an included angle of 5 degrees as shown in the drawing. Cut the 2mm internal keyway. Cut away the excess material from the front side of the crank web. Counter bore from the front to take the maneton bolt head and tap one quarter inch x 32 T.P.I. for the extractor bolt which is used for separating the halves of the crankshaft when it is required to part them.

THE ECCENTRIC SHAFT is the central part of the valve operating gear so that the description of this component will be found in the section dealing with Valve Gear.

THE THRUST BEARING is a single row type which is arranged to take thrust in either direction. Its rear race bears, on its outer edge against a shoulder inside the thrust box and with its inner edge against a distance piece on the crankshaft. The front race bears on its outer edge on a locking ring screwed into an internal thread in the thrust box. The inner edge bears against a distance piece. The sleeves associated with the thrust race act as distance pieces which allow the thrust race an axial movement of .05mm or .002". They must provide free movement of the front and rear races while keeping them centralised.

This arrangement allows .002" axial movement from one thrust situation to an opposite one, allowing the use of either a tractor or pusher propellor. It can be better understood by reference to the oblique section reproduced from the A.M. Handbook in the Appendix.

The crankshaft components.

THE CENTRAL SUPPORT Part No. 9 takes the main weight of the engine and holds the crankshaft in alignment by means of a tapered joint and the key. The central support also carries the contact breakers, the high tension brush and the oil pump. It must be emphasised that the keyways and the key must be a good fit and the crankshaft held firmly on to its taper by the long nut, which is lock wired, as there is a tendency for it to work loose.

The special long extension nut Part No. 13 which draws the crankshaft into the central support is made so that it can be used with all the accessories in place. The nut and the central support are linked by a ring collar so that the nut will also push the crank shaft out of the central support for dismantling.

THE ACCESSORY DRIVE GEARS can now be dealt with as the main 54 tooth gear forms a part of the main crankcase assembly. The gears which drive the magnetos (contact breakers) are 24 tooth which gives the required ratio of two and a quarter to one for the two spark per revolution. The gears have a tooth width of 4mm. The drive to the oil pump is also a 24 tooth gear.

As mentioned before the original model and the description had 36 D.P. gears which is correct for scale. However as 32 D.P. gears are more readily available commercially and later builders have used them the drawings have now been altered to 32 D.P. This results in a small enlargement of the Rear Support, Part No. 9 which is not noticeable. This necessitated a change in the gear centre distances so that the pitch circle on which the magnetos and oil pump are based is changed and the accompanying drawings incorporate this.

MOUNTING STAND

This is a good time to build the engine mounting stand as the engine is taking shape. Its construction is clear from the drawings. It is made from square tube base and 3/8" x quarter inch bore steel tube with actual engine mountings fabricated from sheet. The whole can

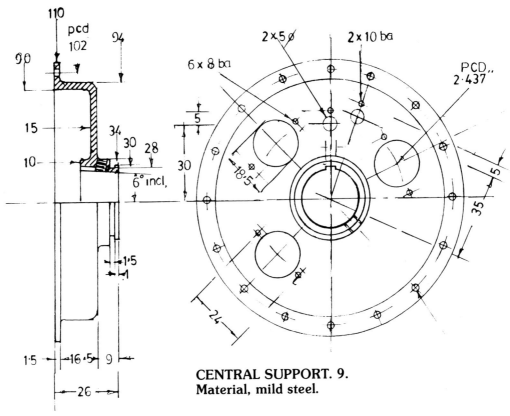

CENTRAL SUPPORT. 9.
Material, mild steel.

be bronze welded together. The photographs give some idea of the arrangement adopted by the Author but is subject to the individual ideas of the builder. The one adopted gives a convenient stand for making adjustments to the breaker points etc and for running the engine.

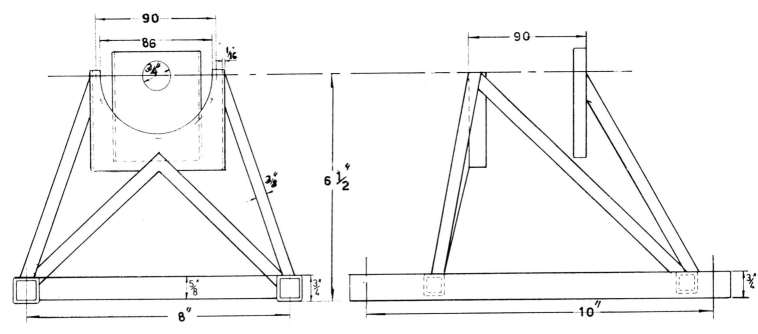

ENGINE MOUNTING STAND.

CYLINDERS

THE CYLINDER BARRELS are of aluminium alloy. Twenty-two fins are machined on the barrels, the depth increasing from the base to the head. Four longitudinal grooves are machined through the fins to clear the holding down bolts.

THE CYLINDER LINERS are of S.G. iron or Meehanite and are shrunk into the barrels. The lip at the top of the liner is clamped firmly between the top of the alloy barrel and cylinder head.

The spigots of the barrel and liner assemblies enter the crankcase seating holes but have to be cut away on each side to clear the adjacent ones and further relieved as required during final assembly to clear the connecting rods.

The cylinders are numbered in a clockwise direction viewed from the front - 1,2,3,4,5,6,7,8,0 as mentioned before. To avoid confusion with the figure 6; the figure 9 is not used.

THE CYLINDER HEADS are machined from the solid in free cutting steel. Each has five circumferential fins which are bevelled off at the front and rear of the head. The induction valve boxes are machined from the solid.

Holes have also to be provided for the two valve rocker posts, for holding down bolts and the two spark plug bosses. The rocker posts are screwed in but must be aligned correctly when tightened down.

FIXTURE FOR MACHINING THE CYLINDER BARRELS CYL-1

The base plate for the fixture used for machining the cylinder barrels is firstly turned a close fit for the recess in the chucking plate which was used for the crankcase fixture. It is then set up on the chucking plate in the lathe and a flat recess turned for seating the end of the cylinder blanks. A clamping ring is turned with its outside diameter a close fit in the recess in the base plate into which it is secured with the four quarter inch N.F. cap screws as shown on drawing. The heads of these must go into counter bores so that their heads are flush with the front face of the ring. The centre is then bored out and the 50mm x 20 T.P.I. thread screw cut into which the cylinder blank will screw. This method ensures that blanks may be relocated in the fixture in exactly the same position each time.

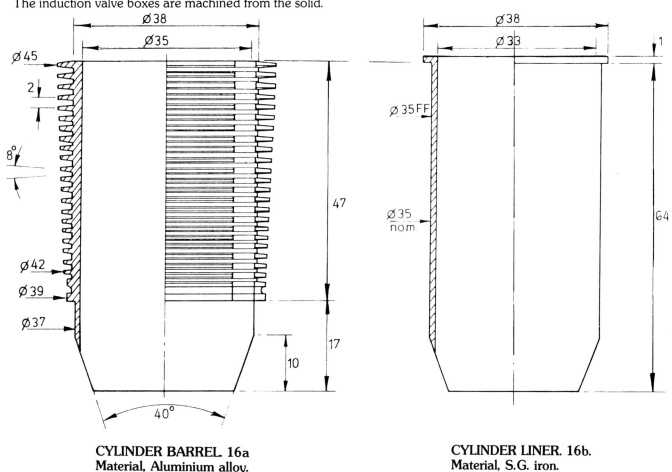

CYLINDER BARREL. 16a
Material, Aluminium alloy.

CYLINDER LINER. 16b.
Material, S.G. iron.

The cylinder barrel blanks are cut from aluminium alloy bar, chucked, and the 50mm x 20 T.P.I. thread screw cut to fit the thread in the clamping ring. The blank is also bored down 40mm diameter x 10mm deep as shown on *Diagram CYL-1*.

The special chucking plate is then set up and a blank screwed into the ring so that it is just proud of the rear face. The four clamping screws are then tightened. The blanks can thus be removed and replaced quickly and accurately so that individual machining operations can be carried out without changing tool positions and angles. The first operation is to rough bore the blanks 30mm diameter through to the previously bored 40mm recess. At the same setting the outside may be machined. All blanks are taken to this stage. From this point all the steps set out below are completed on all the blanks before passing on to the next one.

The cylinder barrel machining fixture.

CYLINDER BARREL MACHINING

1. With a 1mm parting tool part the fin grooves to within 0.5mm of the root diameter of the fins, spacing the cuts by traversing the saddle, taking readings from the graduated index.

2. Finish the sides of the fins with a 6 degree, included angle, tapered form tool to the full depth.

3. Finish the tips of the fins by slightly rounding the corners.

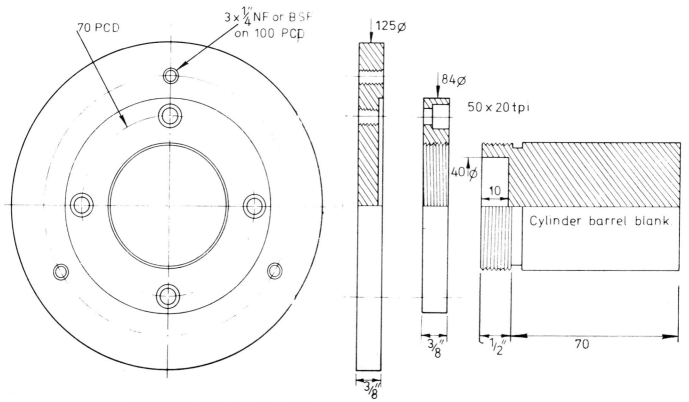

CHUCKING SYSTEM FOR CYLINDER BARRELS.
Diagram CYL-1.

A cylinder barrel blank mounted in the fixture ready for machining.

THE CYLINDER LINERS are machined from solid Flowcast S.G. iron bar or Meehanite. With three inches projecting from the chuck jaws, turn down to 39mm diameter for 70mm. Turn down to 35mm for 64mm. Centre and bore out 32mm for 70mm.

Finish the outside as to the drawing for a light interference fit in the alloy barrel and part off.

Shrink it into the alloy barrel by putting the liner into the freezer and heating the barrel in boiling water. The liners must be pushed home quickly in one push while they remain in this state. Set up in the cylinder finishing fixture and refinish the bore of the liner to 33mm and hone. The finish boring should be done on all the cylinders without disturbing the setting of the boring tool.

CYLINDER HOLDING DOWN STUDS

Machine a point centre on the 3/16" diameter H.T. steel rod held in a collet. Move out sufficient length to machine the full length on the stud, and support the end in the hollow centre in the tailstock. Turn the diameters and thread with the die held in the tailstock die holder. Hold by the thread in a split threaded bush in the collet and turn away the point centre and finish the end. Cut off to length, reverse in the collet and finish the other end.

4. Transfer the whole fixture to the mandrel on the indexing head or rotary table on the milling machine and cut the four grooves length-wise to clear the cylinder holding down bolts with the special milling cutter.

5. Return the fixture to the lathe. Finish the bores to 35mm diameter and part off the cylinders to length. Care must be taken, as the parted off surface forms the seating for the lip of the cylinder liner. Take the corner off the bore with a scraper to clear the radius under the lip on the cylinder liner when it is installed.

The fixture for finishing the cylinders *Diagram CYL-2* is made from a piece of 60mm diameter aluminium alloy bar. Drill and tap four holes on a 45 mm P.C.D. tapped to take 5/32" diam. holding down bolts. It is bored through 34mm diameter to clear the boring tool when taking the finishing cuts through the cylinder liner bores. A recess 0.5mm deep x 38mm diameter is turned on the front face to locate the cylinder liner lip. A ring is made to fit over the cylinder skirt to seat on the cylinder base flange. The cylinder barrel assemblies are in turn mounted in this fixture and the bores finished bored. When the boring tool is set to produce the correct size it should not be disturbed until all the cylinders have been completed. The fixture is now transferred to the indexing head or rotary table on the milling machine and the bevels cut in the skirt at an angle of 20 degrees so that they do not interfere with the adjacent cylinders when they are in position on the crankcase. The cuts must be made with a light feed to avoid distortion.

The cylinder barrel finishing fixture.

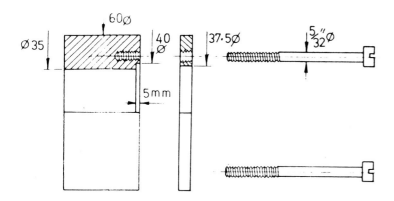

CYLINDER BARREL FINISHING JIG.
Diagram CYL-2.

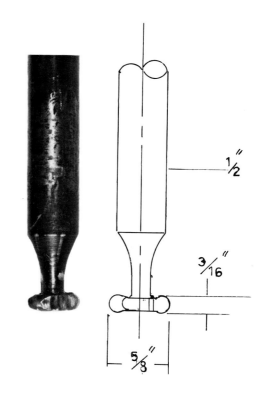

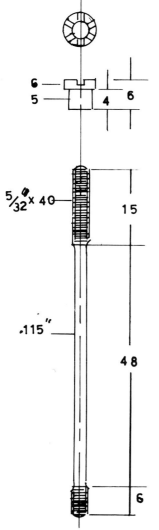

CYLINDER HOLDING DOWN STUDS.
Material,   H. T. steel.

The cutter for grooving the cylinder barrel fins to clear the holding down bolt.

A cylinder barrel and cylinder head.

CYLINDER HEADS

CYLINDER HEAD MACHINING FIXTURE

A half inch thick base plate has a recess turned in the top face to locate the two and a half inch diameter mounting pad to which it is secured by four 1/4" socket head screws. These enter counterbored holes from the bottom and screw into holes tapped in the mounting pad. The base plate has four holes drilled to take bolts which secure it to the rotary table. It also has four holes tapped 1/4" N.F. to secure the pedestals which take the cylinder head securing screws. These screws have 60 degree pointed ends and are case hardened. They engage in centre holes drilled round the periphery of the blank. The centre lines of these screws are on a slightly lower plane than the holes. They engage to ensure that the blanks are held down securely when tightened.

The mounting pad has a 5/32" hole drilled which carries a locating pin. This engages one of the cylinder head holding down bolt holes to secure it against radial movement.

The pedestals are made from 1/4" thick steel angle. The upper portion must be bevelled as shown to allow clearance for the milling cutter to approach the blank.

EXHAUST VALVE CAGE

Before machining the cylinder heads the exhaust valve cages should be made. At this stage the legs forming the spider are not machined; this is done after

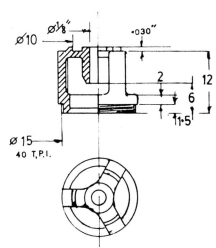

EXHAUST VALVE CAGE. (15).

the cages are screwed in and swaged into the heads. This is the reason that left hand threads are specified so that the action of the milling cutter tends to tighten the cages onto their seats rather than unscrew them, with disastrous results. It also of course ensures that the legs of the cage are correctly positioned. As a special tap has to be made in any case, it is just as easy to make a left hand one. In the case of screwing the cages one is also thread cutting away from a shoulder.

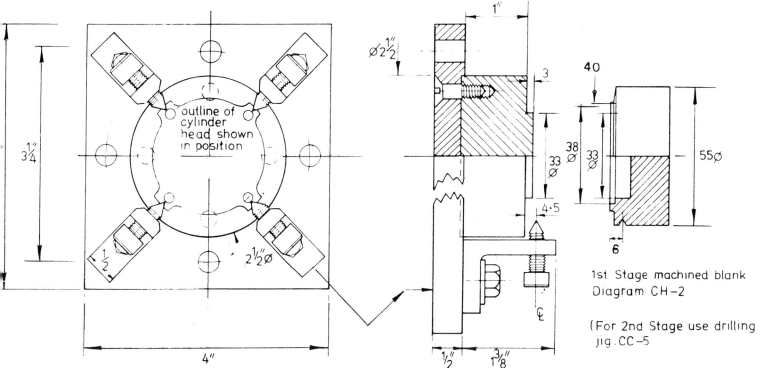

1st Stage machined blank
Diagram CH-2

(For 2nd Stage use drilling jig. CC-5

CYLINDER HEAD MACHINING FIXTURE.
Diagram CH-1.

MACHINING THE CYLINDER HEADS

The cylinder heads are produced from solid blanks of free cutting steel 54mm diameter x 24mm long. The first operation is to face the blank. This face will be used as the base reference for all further machining operations. While the blank is set up in the lathe the combustion chamber is machined out 33mm diameter x 9mm deep. The recess for the lip of the cylinder liner which locates the head centrally on the cylinder barrel assembly and what will be the bottom side of the lower cooling fin are also completed. *Diagram CH-1.*

A mark is made round the blank 5mm from the base reference with a sharp pointed tool. On this line, index and drill 4 holes with a centre drill for the clamping dogs to engage. These secure the blank to the machining fixture, CH-1. This completes the preparatory work on the lathe and all blanks can be brought to this stage before proceeding.

Cylinder head, showing volute valve spring.

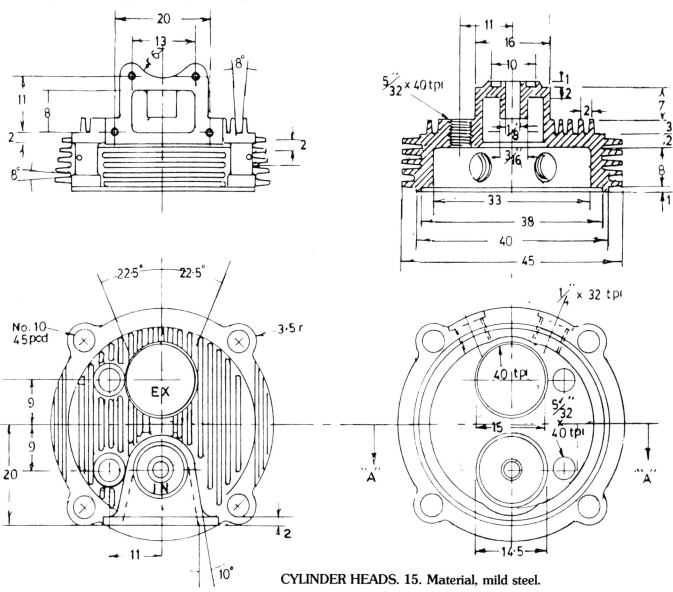

CYLINDER HEADS. 15. Material, mild steel.

40

The next operation is carried out by clamping the *drilling jig CC-5* over the combustion chamber. Drill the four No. 30 diameter holes on a 45mm pitch circle for the holding down bolts. When the first one is drilled insert a locating pin to prevent the blank moving. Drill two No. 29 holes for the valve rocker post holes. To form the inside of the inlet valve box and valve guide drill down through the jig with a half inch drill until the tip of the drill is at a depth of 12mm below the base reference. Follow with the special hollow cutter 'F' to a depth of 19mm below the base reference. This completes the inside of the inlet valve box and valve guide. The exhaust valve port can be drilled right through the blank with a half inch drill. This is opened out later to 9/16" diameter. Insert the drill bush in the jig and drill a No. 31 hole right through to form the inlet valve guide. Remove the jig and tap the two No. 29 holes 5/32 x 40 tpi. to take the valve rocker posts. These must be tapped truly vertical and can be done while the work is still at the drill press. Ream the valve guide 1/8". Open out the exhaust port to 9/16" and chamfer the hole so that the valve cage can be swaged out slightly to secure it. Tap the port 15mm x 40 tpi. with a left hand thread.

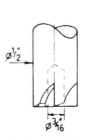

Shell mill for forming the valve guides in the cylinder heads
Diagram CH-1(a)

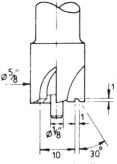

Cutter for forming the valve spring locating ribs on the top of the valve box and spider
Diagram CH-1(b)

CYLINDER HEAD TOOLS.

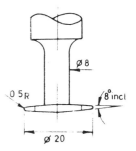

Cutter for milling the horizontal fins
Diagram CH-1(d)

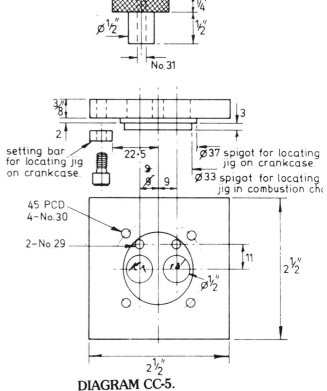

DIAGRAM CC-5.
Cylinder head & crankcase drilling jig.

Cylinder head.

The next operation is carried out by mounting the blanks on *milling fixture CH-9*. The blank is located over the spigot and held from rotation by a peg engaging one of the cylinder holding down bolt holes. The same hole in each blank must be selected and used on subsequent remountings to ensure uniform location. The blank is held down securely on to the fixture by equally tightening the clamping dogs which are engaged in the centre holes previously drilled for them.

The vertical movement of the cutter as described is relative to the base reference line of the cylinder head. All reference settings were made by using the vertical movement of the table. The quill movement was used to withdraw the cutter clear of the work and fixture to allow the rotary table to be rotated for the next cut. The quill stop was firmly fixed so that the cutter could be returned to its former level for resumption of the work.

The *milling fixture CH-1* is set up on the rotary table on the vertical milling machine.

With a standard 3/8" end mill remove as much surface material as possible down to a level of 21mm above base reference which is the level of the top of the valve spring locating rib on top of the valve boxes. The top surface is blued and the outlines of the inlet valve box again marked out with the aid of the marking out button. The surplus material is now removed around the outer limits of the inlet valve box and the inlet box flange down to a level of 14mm above the base reference, which is the level of the top of the vertical fins. Extreme caution must be used in planning the cuts to leave valve boxes and flange intact.

Machining the valve spring retaining ribs.

The face of the inlet box flange can now be machined down to a level of 9mm above the base reference. This leaves the lower four fins intact. The profiling cutter 'd' with the .120" pilot is then used to form the valve spring locating rib *Diagram CH-3-4*. The area round the exhaust valve port is now spotfaced with the special spotfacer.

An alternate method of dealing with the exhaust valve port is to leave it at half inch diameter until the work with the drilling jig etc is completed. The head can

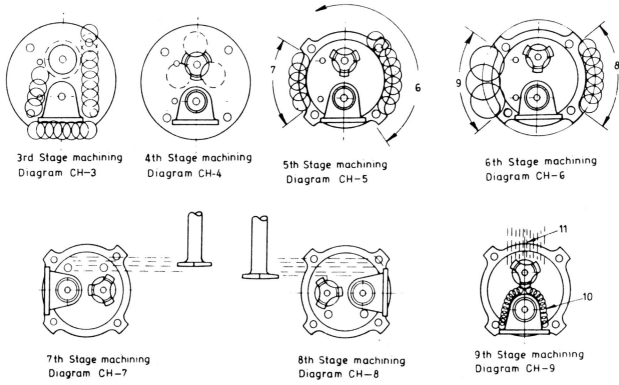

3rd Stage machining
Diagram CH–3

4th Stage machining
Diagram CH–4

5th Stage machining
Diagram CH–5

6th Stage machining
Diagram CH–6

7th Stage machining
Diagram CH–7

8th Stage machining
Diagram CH–8

9th Stage machining
Diagram CH–9

CYLINDER HEAD MACHINING PROCEDURES.
Diagrams CH-3 to 9.

Machining round the ends of the vertical fins, at the same time finishing the tops of the holding down bosses.

Machining the 4 degrees taper on the upper surface of the top fin.

the required radius. The total distance is of course the specified radius plus the outside diameter of the cutter divided by 2. This is the working setting which must be noted and marked. The table is further moved so that the cutter will clear the blank and the jig. It is then lowered to its working position against the stop setting of the quill.

The cut is then initiated by feeding the cutter in to the previously recorded and marked position. The flow of cutting oil must be started before cutting commences.

Machining the horizontal fins.

be set up on a simple fixture mounted in the chuck in the lathe. The half inch hole can then be bored out with a boring tool and the thread cut and upper face trued up to a smooth seat to take the valve cage. The partly finished exhaust valve cages can then be screwed into the cylinder heads and swaged permanently into position with the special swaging tool. The head is then returned to the milling fixture and a half inch end mill used with great care to remove the metal between the legs of the exhaust valve cage. At this stage the cylinder head is set with its centre coincident with the axis of the rotary table.

To position the cutter radially the axis of the rotary table must be made to coincide with the axis of the milling machine spindle. The cross slide is then locked up. The reading of the micrometer index for the longitudinal movement is then adjusted to zero. This forms the basic reference for setting the cutter to cut at

Machining the vertical fins with the rotary table in the vertical position front side. Note how the front ends of the horizontal fins have been tapered off to clear the valve push rods. The rear ends have been tapered in the same way.

A 3/8" standard end mill can now be used to form the radius 3mm deep which will become the ends of the vertical fins. It is set to cut at a radius of 19mm down to a depth of 11mm above the base reference, again avoiding the inlet flange, box and the exhaust cage. *Diagram CH-5/6.* This cut also forms the top of the holding down bosses.

Again with the standard 3/8" end mill profile the outside diameter of the area which will form the tips of the fins to a radius of 22.5 diameter, leaving the bosses for the cylinder holding down bolts. *Diagram CH-6.* If desired to bush the valve guide the holes can be opened out and bronze bushes fitted.

The special 4 degree end mill is now used to finish off the upper taper of the top fin between the bosses. *Diagram CH-6.*

Spot facing the sparking plug holes.

Machining the vertical fins on the rear side.

Change to the special fin groove milling cutter with the included angle of 8 degrees to cut the fin grooves between the holding down bosses. *Diagram CH-6.* The cylinder head must be centralised with the cutter and locked. The table is then traversed so that the tip of the cutter is set to cut on a radius of 20mm when the rotary table is operated. The reading of the graduated index should be noted so that it can be returned to this position. The table is then traversed so that the blank is clear of the cutter.

Lower the cutter onto the upper surface of the machining fixture onto which the blank is clamped. This is the base reference and the quill stop is set. The table is then lowered 2mm so that the cutter is in a position to cut the first fin groove. The cutter is then fed in to the predetermined setting with the rotary table positioned to clear a holding bolt boss. The angular reading on the rotary table is noted and the groove is cut by rotating

the blank, stopping short of the next boss. A log of all these readings must be kept so that the procedures can be repeated. *Diagram CH-5/9.*

When the four cuts to form the first fin are completed the table is lowered a further 2mm for each successive fin groove. The cut is increased by 1mm for grooves 2, 3 and 4 so that the cutter tips are working on a radius of 18mm from the centre of the blank. In the case of the grooves on the spark plug side the cut will probably be no more than a plunge cut to the specified depth without any radial movement being required.

Machining out the inlet port from the flange to the inlet valve box.

The ends of the horizontal fins on the front and rear faces must be trimmed off to a tapered profile as shown in the drawing. Those on the front must clear the push rods over their range of movement.

The rotary table is now secured on the milling machine table in a vertical position taking care that it is aligned accurately. It is set and locked so that the vertical fins may cut to a depth of 3mm as in *Diagrams CH-7, 8 & 9,* leaving the lands around the valve rocker post holes. Extreme caution must be used to avoid damaging previously finished parts. The blank can then be set round by rotating the table to the required position for drilling, tapping and spot facing the spark plug bosses.

With the inlet port flange at the top, the inlet passage from the face of the flange into the inlet box may be opened up using a 3/16" slot drill, taking care not to damage the valve guide when breaking through. *Photograph CH-9.* While in this position jig drill the tapping size holes in the inlet flange 4 x No.55 and tap 10BA. A drilling jig is used for this purpose and is also used to mark out the profile of the outer limits of the flange. It is located from its lower edge resting on the upper side of the cooling fin. The outline of the flange is profiled by filing.

Left; The cutter for forming the 4 deg. taper on the upper side of the cylinder head top fins. Right; The fin groove cutter for machining the fins on both the sides and the top of the heads.

The short fins on the spark plug side of the head near the exhaust valve are now cut with the special 4 degrees angle slot mill as shown in *Diagram CH-8/11.* There may be some cleaning up of the fins already cut required while this cutter is mounted.

The rotary table is now returned to the horizontal position and a cut taken round the base of the induction valve box to a level 11mm above the base reference, with a 1/8" diameter end mill as shown in *Diagram CH-8/10.*

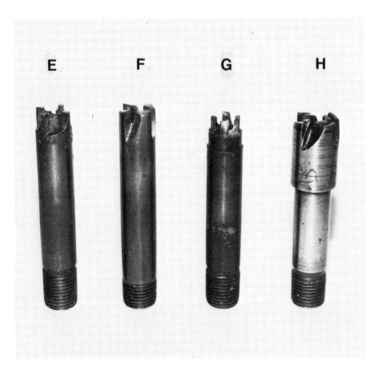

E. *Hollow milling cutter used with an inserted pilot for finishing the ends of the rocker pivot bosses on the rocker posts. F. Shell mill used for forming the valve guide bosses. G. Not used. H. special mill for cutting down and forming the rib on the valve box and spider to hold the valve springs central.*

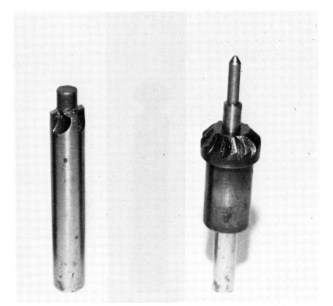

Left; Spot facer for the spark plug holes. Right; Valve seat cutter.

The bosses for the holding down bolt holes must be finished by rotating them against a standard ⅜" end mill. The centre for rotating them is a pin on a special fixture attached to the milling machine table which enters the holding down bolt holes. This process must be repeated to remove the metal from the central portion of the boss with a special cutter.

From Left; The exhaust valve cage seat spotfacer. The special L.H. tap for the exhaust valve cage. The swaging tool for the exhaust valve cages.

VALVE GEAR

VALVE GEAR OPERATION

Diagram V.G.1. shows the action of the valve operating gear. The inlet and exhaust valve systems are identical. The exhaust system is situated in front of the inlet.

The 18-tooth gear ring 'A' is fixed inside the cam box and together with the tappets revolves round the centre 'B'.

The 16-tooth gear 'C' rotates on the eccentric 'D' which is keyed to the forward part of the maneton shaft which does not rotate. Gear 'C' has four of its teeth extended to form the tappet lifting points 1,2,3, & 4 in the diagram. The line B - E - F - represents the mid point of the valve open period.

If the gear ring 'A' is turned through one conmplete revolution in the direction of the arrow, the 16-tooth gear 'C' will roll around inside the 18-tooth gear ring 'A' and will therefore complete one and one eighth revolutions while 'A' completes one revolution. The tappet 'F' being carried around with 'A', will also complete one revolution, and will have returned to the position shown; but it will now fall between cam points 1 and 2, because 'C' has turned through one and one eighth revolutions. However because 'C' has advanced one eighth of a revolution on 'A', tappet 'F' will now lie midway between cams 1 and 2. After a further revolution of 'A', tappet 'F' will rest on cam 2. As the distance between each pair of tappets is one eighth of the circumference of the gear ring, i.e., two teeth, and the distance between each pair of cam points is one quarter of the circumference of the gear, i.e., four teeth, the cams will operate each alternate tappet in order; the timing sequence will, therefore, be 1,3,5,7,0, 2,4,6,8. The reproduced drawings from the Bentley engine handbook will help to make this clear.

VALVE GEAR COMPONENTS

The cam gear box revolves on two ball bearings carried on the cam gear shaft. This shaft is pushed over and keyed to the front extension of the maneton shaft. Between these bearings are the eccentrics which carry the inlet and exhaust, 16-tooth internally toothed rings which rotate with the cam case, being keyed to it and located endwise by distance pegs. It should be noted that the position of the keyway in the housing is in axial alignment with the inlet tappet guide of number 1 cylinder. The position of the spacing of the pegs on the exhaust gear ring is displaced circumferentially 20 degrees from those on the inlet gear ring as shown on the drawing. This is to clear the exhaust tappets which are displaced circumferentially 20 degrees from the inlet tappets.

The inlet and exhaust valve rockers are carried on posts which are screwed into the cylinder heads. The outer ends of these posts are forked. The rocker pivot pins are pressed into the rockers and pivot in the fork ends. The valve end of each rocker is forked and is fitted with a hardened steel roller, working on a hardened pin which is a press fit in one side of the fork. The outer ends of the rockers have a spherical socket which takes the ball on the push rod ends.

The push rods are of hollow stainless steel tube into which are screwed adjustable ball fittings with lock nuts at each end. The thimbles on the outer end of the tappets hold the push rod ends captive and their length is such that the inner movement of the tappet is restricted so that it does not come into contact with the cam gear on the alternate revolution during which the valve must remain seated.

THE OUTER RING GEARS are made from 0.0625" thick gauge plate. The 18 teeth have a circular pitch of

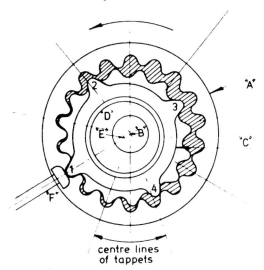

centre lines
of tappets

Diagram VG 1.

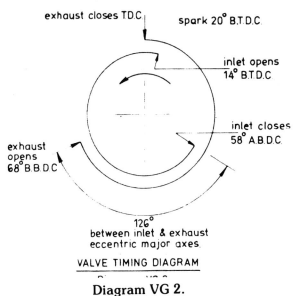

VALVE TIMING DIAGRAM

Diagram VG 2.

Front view of the engine with the propellor shaft and front bearing carrier removed to show the exhaust cam gear and gear ring. The inlet gear pack can just be seen lying behind it.

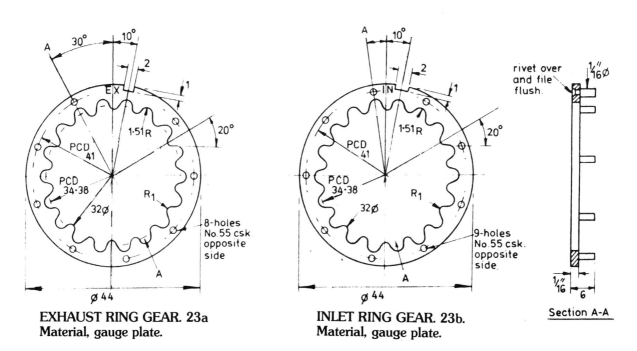

EXHAUST RING GEAR. 23a
Material, gauge plate.

INLET RING GEAR. 23b.
Material, gauge plate.

Section A-A

6mm which gives a pitch circle diameter of 34.38mm. Cut out two squares of the plate 50mm square. Grip in the four jaw chuck with soft packing behind on the rotary table. Centralise with the milling spindle and displace by PCD/2 = 17.19mm.

With a 1/8" diameter centre drill in the chuck, drill a row of 18 holes on the pitch circle. Displace a further 3mm to spot 9 holes at 20.5mm radius opposite every alternate hole previously drilled. These are to mark the centres of the No. 55 holes later to be drilled and counter sunk for the distance pegs which space the cam rings from one another and the distance piece.

Transfer the chuck to the lathe, bore out the centre to 32mm diameter and part off the disc leaving the outside diameter 44mm.

Finish the teeth by filing the flanks to an angle of 20 degrees and rounding the tops to a radius of 1mm. The final finishing can be done when a partial assembly can be made with the cam gears. Temporary spacing pegs can be fitted for this purpose. Any binding can be relieved by filing the teeth on the ring gears before they are hardened.

Drill and counter sink the 9 x No.55 holes previously spotted for the distance pegs. File the keyway on the outside diameter. Harden and temper after the final finishing.

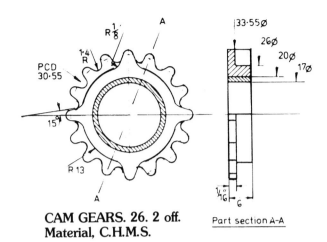

CAM GEARS. 26. 2 off.
Material, C.H.M.S.

Part section A-A

Rivet the distance pegs into the ring, filing off the surplus flush with the surface.

THE CAM GEARS are made from case hardening steel. The 16 teeth have a circular pitch of 6mm giving a pitch circle diameter of 30.55mm.

Chuck with sufficient material clear of the jaws to mill the extended teeth on the cam gears.

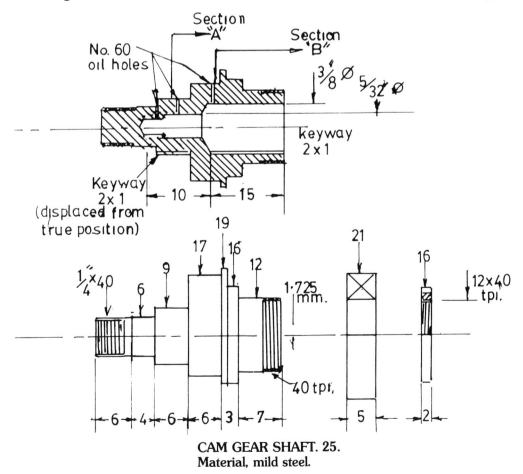

CAM GEAR SHAFT. 25.
Material, mild steel.

Drill 16 No. 35 holes 8mm deep on a radius of 15.27mm. These holes form the roots of the teeth.

Turn down to 34mm diameter the full width of the finished cam gear.

Mill the tops of the teeth with the special profiling cutter. The profiling cutter is made by turning the groove with a form tool. This is a 1/8" diameter button mounted on a shank which is fed into the centre of a quarter inch wide blank a total distance of 0.1". Each side of the groove is then flared out to an angle of 15 degrees until the straight meets the tangent of the groove. The teeth are then cut by milling and the cutter hardened. The tops of the teeth on the cam gear are then finished. With a quarter inch mill, mill the surplus material on the back of the cam gear to a depth of 4.5mm, and a radius of 13mm leaving the four extended teeth intact.

Bore the centre to 20mm diameter. Part off and finish the back of the cam gear by mounting on a stub mandrel.

The gear is then case hardened and the bronze bush fitted.

THE ECCENTRIC SHAFT

Chuck a 1" bar of mild steel leaving 2" projecting. Turn down the 19mm flange and 17mm diameter for chucking piece inlet eccentric.

Chuck in the four jaw, off-set to give the previously turned inlet eccentric a throw of 3.45mm.

Turn the rear end to fit the ball bearing and thread 40 T.P.I. to take the retaining nut. Bore out to fit the maneton shaft extension. Drill down a further 10mm x 5/32 diameter. Cut off.

Make a threaded chucking piece to accept the rear end of the eccentric shaft. Screw in the partly finished eccentric shaft and finish the front end to take the exhaust cam, front cam box bearing and screw cut a quarter inch x 40 T.P.I. to take the front nut.

Make the exhaust eccentric the same throw as the inlet to fit the eccentric shaft. Cut the key-way in its bore on the major axis of the cam.

The whole valve timing of the engine *Diagram VG-2* is dependent on the accurate positioning of the key-ways.

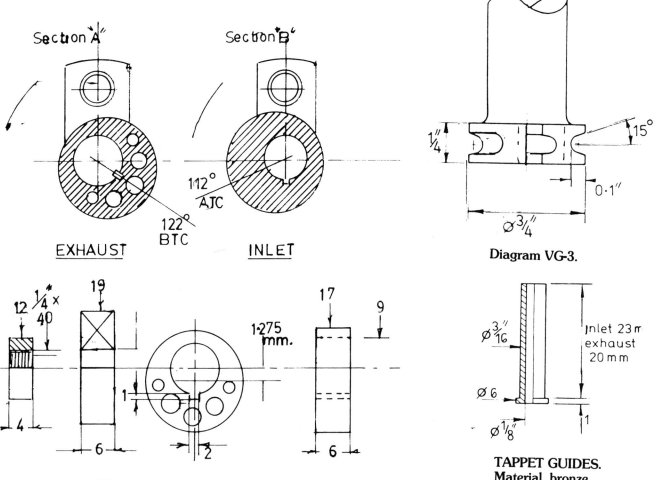

Section 'A"   Section 'B'

112°
ATC

122°
BTC

EXHAUST   INLET

EXHAUST ECCENTRIC. 24.
Material, mild steel.

Diagram VG-3.

TAPPET GUIDES.
Material, bronze.

50

Make an adaptor to fit on the inlet cam with a flange eccentric by 3.45mm to hold a timing protractor, so that it runs true when the eccentric shaft is set up to run on its normal axis.

The protractor zero mark must line up with the major-minor axes of the inlet cam. The cam can be set round the required number of degrees and the internal keyway to mate with the maneton shaft keyway planed with a 1mm cutter.

The eccentric shaft is then reversed, held in another chucking piece and the keyway for the exhaust cam machined, measuring the required number of degrees from the zero on the protractor.

The keyways are positioned so that the cams are at the highest point of their lift midway between the opening and closing of their respective valves.

Oil holes are drilled as shown on the drawing to convey oil from the centre of the maneton shaft to the various parts of the valve gear.

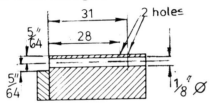

TAPPET MACHINING JIG.
Diagram TF-1.
Mild steel, case hardened.

THE TAPPET FINISHING JIG

A 1/8" diameter hole is drilled lengthwise in a piece of steel a half inch x 3/4". The centre of the hole is 3/16" from one side. Across the jig drill two No. 60 holes to intercept the centre line of the 1/8" hole. These holes must be located so that the holes in the ends of the tappets may be drilled the required distance from the head, firstly for the inlet tappets and then for the exhaust tappets.

The top of the jig is then milled down so that the face of the jig is 0.078" from the centre of the hole. A 1/8" pin can be put in the hole and a .016" feeler gauge should just be gripped by a flat surface on the face being milled when the correct level is reached. The jig is then case hardened.

TAPPETS

The maximum lift of the tappet must be restricted to the height of the cam gear tooth because every alternate revolution the bottom of the tappet must clear the base circle of the cam gear when it comes around. The tappet thimbles limit the inward movement by coming into contact with the outer end of the tappet guides. The free length of the tappet and thimble assembly must be such that this occurs. The degree to which the outer ends of the tappet guides project also affects the travel of the tappet.

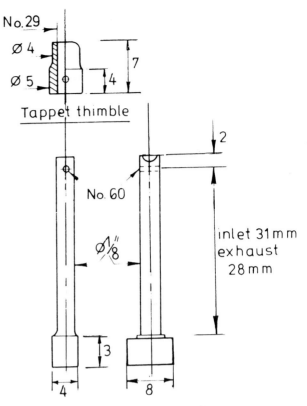

TAPPETS. Inlet & Exhaust. 35.
Material, silver steel.

The tappets are machined from silver steel by supporting the outer end on a spherical centre held in the tail stock. The centre in the tappet is formed by a special spherical ended bit. This centre becomes the socket for the lower end of the push rod. The tappets are then inserted in the jig and one side of the head filed down level with the top face of the jig. When they have all been done an alignment block is then sweated onto the end to hold the flat already filed so that the opposite side may be filed at 180 degrees down to a symmetrical level.

The jig is then used to drill the No. 60 pin holes for retaining the valve tappet thimbles.

It will be noted that the inlet and exhaust tappets are different in length.

ROCKER POSTS

Mount a half inch diameter steel bar in a collet on the dividing head on the milling machine.
Centre and cross drill a No. 32 hole through 19mm from the end. This hole becomes the main rocker pivot and will be reamed 1/8".

Spot face to form the ends of the pivot bosses from each side indexing 180 degrees to leave the finished length 10mm overall.

Mill flats 8mm apart at 90 degrees to previously milled flats.

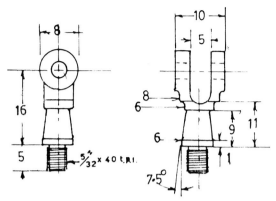

ROCKER POSTS. 19.
Material, mild steel.

Centre and drill through 3/16" diameter at a distance of 4mm from the centre of the previously drilled 1/8" hole. This forms the jaw of the rocker post when the opening is later cut out to take the rocker.

Transfer to the lathe and turn the pillar to 8mm diameter for a length of 16mm. Turn the tapered portion of the pillar to an included angle of 15 degrees. Turn 5mm length 5/32" diam. Undercut 1mm to thread depth and thread 40 T.P.I.

The rocker posts must be lined up so that the pivot holes are aligned correctly when screwed home tight into their seating in the cylinder heads. Each one is fitted individually and marked so that it will be installed in the same hole on assembly. The correct position can be achieved while the rocker post is still chucked in the collet by screwing the head onto the thread so that it seats home. Adjustment may be made by skimming some metal off the base and again trying. The amount to be taken off is quite small as the post faces correctly twice each turn which is an axial movement of .0125". The removal of .001" therefore results in an angular movement of 15 degrees.

The final job is to round off the ends of the rocker pivot bosses by swinging them on a pivot in the milling machine against a 3/8" diameter end mill. A handle tapped 5/32" x 40 T.P.I. in one end is used to control the movement.

The fork end is finally formed by sawing down to the hole which forms the bottom of the fork and finishing by filing.

The posts are locked into place on final assembly of the cylinder heads by a centre pop swelling some metal from the cylinder head into a nick cut into the end of each post.

VALVE ROCKERS

These are of built up construction. The main web is of 1/16" thick gauge plate which is drilled with the aid of a simple *jig. VG-4.* The jig is designed to take a length of 1/16" gauge plate 1" wide of sufficient length to make all the rockers required.

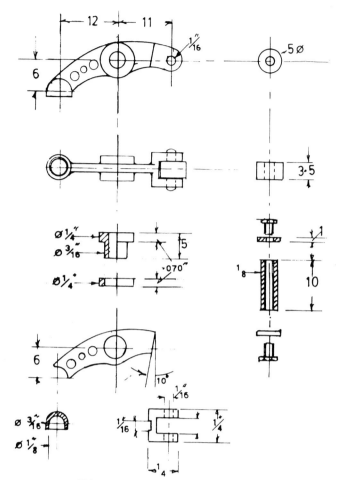

VALVE ROCKERS. 19.
Material gauge plate.

The jig is made from a 2" length of 1" x 3/8" steel bar. The holes are drilled and tapped 3/16" to take the clamping screws. The slot 1 1/16" wide is then milled across to receive the stock gauge plate. The holes are then laid out and drilled and the whole case hardened. When drilling the stock it can be supported on some 1" wide hard wood on the drill press table.

The jig is located by a peg in the locating hole and clamped with the two screws. After drilling the set of holes the jig is then loosened and moved along the stock until the locating peg will enter the previously drilled main rocker hole. After drilling all the holes the individual rockers are then cut off and shaped. It is probably worth while to shape a spare one and harden it out and use this as a filing guide.

The fork end is made from a length of quarter inch square key steel. The first operation is to mill a groove central to one side the full length, 1/16" wide by 1/32" deep to take the end of the web. The bar is then turned over and the groove to form the fork end is milled the full length 1/8" wide by 3/16" deep. The holes for the 1/16" diameter roller pins can then be drilled with the aid of a simple drilling jig before cutting off 7/32" long.

The sockets for the push rod ends are a straight forward turning job.

The whole assembly is then held in the fixture for silver soldering the component parts, using the minimum amount of silver solder. It is then cleaned up and the finishing done including rounding off the fork ends. The final job is to have them all satin chrome plated.

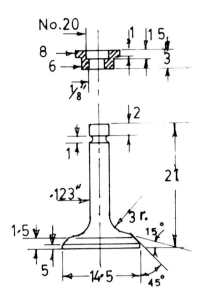

**VALVES –Inlet & Exhaust. 20.
Material, stainless steel.**

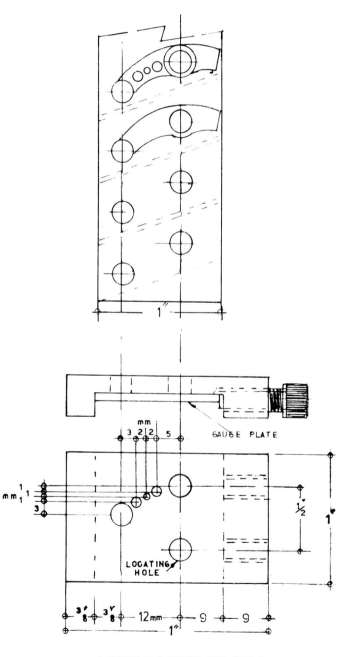

VALVE ROCKER JIG. VG-4.

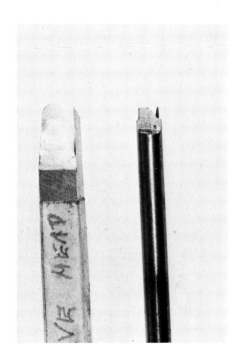

Left; Tool for forming the heads of the valves. Right; The female centre for turning the valves.

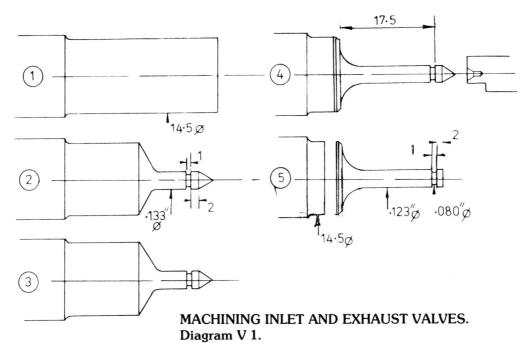

MACHINING INLET AND EXHAUST VALVES.
Diagram V 1.

VALVE SPRING CAPS are retained on the valve stems by circlips. The circlips are of soft wire. They are made by winding a length on a mandrel and cutting through the individual turns. The circlips fit into the grooves in the valve stems. In this position they will be a close fit in the bore of the valve spring caps. They are made from No. 20 S.W.G.

VALVE ROCKER SHAFTS. Rollers and roller pins are made from silver steel and hardened and tempered to a light blue.

PUSH RODS

The push rods are made from stainless steel tubing 3.25mm outside diameter and 2.2mm inside diameter. They are cut to length and tapped each end 6BA for the ball end fittings.

The ball fittings have two flats milled adjacent to the ball to hold them from turning when adjustment is being made. Lock nuts are fitted to secure the adjustment.

The ball end at the inner end of the push rod is held captive on to the tappet by means of the tappet thimble which is swaged down over the ball end with a bell mouth swaging tool. It is passed over the threaded portion. The swaging should only be carried to the stage at which the ball end is positively held captive but has sufficient movement. The tappet thimble is in turn held on to the top of the tappet by the cross pin.

VOLUTE VALVE SPRINGS are very characteristic of the period of the Bentley and of the period in general; a volute spring has the advantage of contracting within itself and so saving something in overall height as

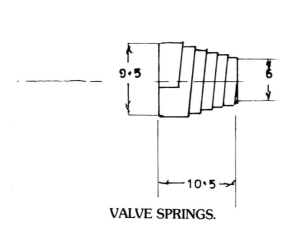

VALVE SPRINGS.

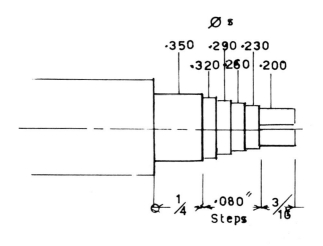

Lead set at 12 T.P.I.
VALVE SPRING MANDREL

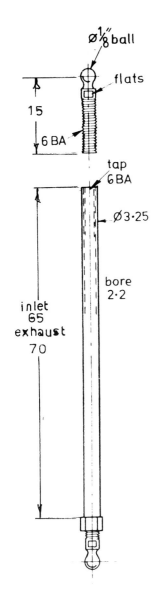

PUSH RODS. 18.
Material, s.s.

Two views showing the set up for winding the volute valve springs from strip material.

against a conventional coil spring. The Bentley springs are made from flat strip and to use wire springs rather spoils the otherwise accurate reproduction of the original.

The first problem in producing the springs is in the procurement of suitable spring steel strip. The obvious avenue seemed to be the Watch and Clock Trade. After some trial and error a satisfactory strip was obtained, but not in strip form. The product originates almost entirely from Switzerland and was only obtainable as ready made-up coils as clock springs. However in the end this was no problem. The drawing gives the desired dimensions of the finished spring.

It is recommended that the springs be made before the mating parts in case there is any discrepancy in the finished sizes (diameters) of the springs. The spring strip

is 4.0mm x .3mm and each coil made four finished springs so six coils are required.

The actual coiling is done in the lathe on a stepped mandrel. By winding the lathe backwards by hand and set in bottom backgear position, the lathe saddle is traversed by engaging the lead screw which is set for 12 T.P.I. It is necessary to make a tool post mounted fixture as illustrated in *Diagram VS-1*. This fixture provides a pressure pad which applies some tension to the strip as it feeds onto the mandrel, also guide pins lead the strip at the 12 T.P.I. rate and on the top of the fixture is mounted the butane burner which is a Primus No. 8318.

The strip which is of course already hardened and tempered is not preannealed but is fed via the restraining pressure pad past the butane burner which brings the strip locally to a medium red heat (850 degrees C) immediately before it is coiled onto the stepped mandrel. When starting it is necessary to soften the tip of the strip so that a right angle bend can be made which is slipped into the slot in the end of the mandrel.

The operation is essentially a two-man job, one to light and control the burner and the other to wind the lathe at such a rate that the strip maintains the red heat just before coiling. Quite fortuitously it was found that in winding onto the relatively cool mandrel the spring steel strip chilled enough to restore the desired spring temper and no further heat treatment was necessary.

After the coiling is complete it is only necessary to grind the ends of the spring square, the small starting bend can be cracked off with a pair of long-nose pliers and the finishing end may be feathered off for appearance.

The mandrel itself does not require any description other than the drawing provided. The jig to carry the pressure pad and the butane burner will depend on the actual equipment being used and the drawings are only typical of what is required.

Front view of the cylinder and head assembly.

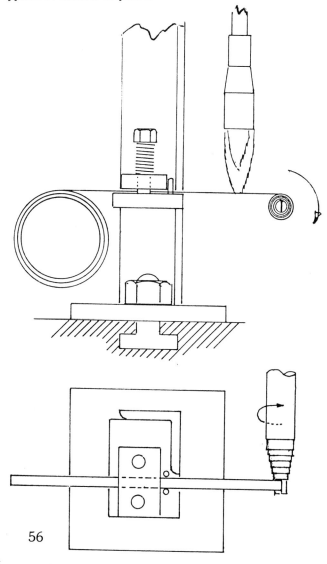

Left. Diagram VS-1.

56

CONNECTING RODS

MASTER CONNECTING ROD

Machine the central big end drum. Index, drill and ream the 9 holes for the wrist pins.

Machine the master rod proper finishing it to fit closely between the cheeks of the big end drum. This rod is made the same as the slave rods except for the inner end which is fitted closely to the drum and secured by a quarter inch diameter shear pin corresponding to the wrist pin on the slave rods. There is also a 1/8" diameter alignment pin to provide additional security.

The two items should be tinned before assembly and the whole finally secured by inserting the pin and sweating the entire assembly together. An alternative method of securing the parts is with Loctite. Drill down from the gudgeon pin end with a 1/16" drill sweated into a quarter inch diameter extension shank breaking right through into the bore of the big end as shown in the drawing.

The master and slave connecting rod array.

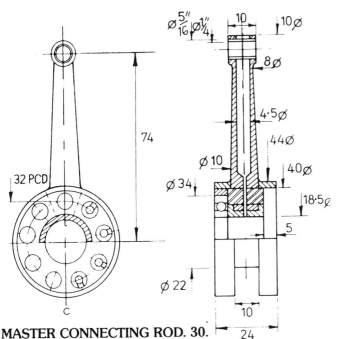

MASTER CONNECTING ROD. 30.
Material, H.T. steel.

SLAVE CONNECTING RODS

Material; 5/8" diameter high tensile steel. Drill a 5/16" diameter cross hole in the end of the bar. Chuck in the three jaw with sufficient length projecting to make one connecting rod. Centre drill the end and bring up the rear centre. Turn the central portion of the rod as shown on the drawings leaving the ends of sufficient diameter to mill the flat which form the ends of the wrist and gudgeon pin bosses. Drill 3/16" diameter up the length of the rod to just short of the wrist pin hole.

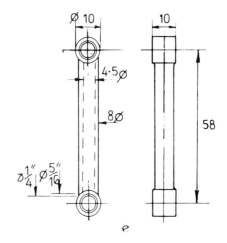

SLAVE RODS. 30.
Material, H.T. steel.

Make a locating post as shown on *Diagram No. CR-1* to secure in the 'T' slot in the milling machine table. It is threaded 1/2" N.F. for a nut to clamp upright in the 'T' slot. It also takes a nut with a lock nut to bring up and support the ends of the connecting rods while the flats are being milled. The plain portion of the supporting post should be a good fit in the cross holes of the connecting rods. It should be arranged so that it is capable of supporting the outer end of the rods when the bar is held in the vee blocks as shown in *Diagram No. CR-1.*

The bar to which the blank is still attached is clamped on vee blocks on the table with the hole over the locating post which has been previously positioned directly under the centre of the milling machine spindle. The bar must be aligned with the milling machine table and the cross slide locked. The reading of the graduated index must be noted so that the table can be returned to this position. The flats are then milled with a 5/8" diameter end mill. Returning the table to centre zero, the table is traversed the required centre to centre distance of 58mm by the graduated dial. The second cross hole is then drilled and opened out to 5/16" diameter.

Turn the blank over and raise the supporting nuts on the jig post to contact the lower face and mill the other side of the blank. The jig post ensures that the two transverse holes are in alignment.

Cut off the connecting rod from the bar and finish by grinding and filling off all the surplus material to the finished state.

Press in the wrist pin bush and drill the oil hole through with the 1/16" drill on the extension shank. This hole must go right through and out the end of the connecting rod.

A 1/16" diameter oil hole must be drilled through one side of the gudgeon pin bush. When the bush is installed the oil hole must face the connecting rod shank.

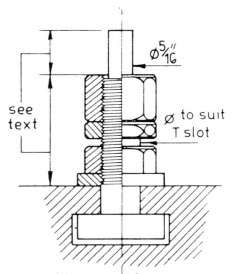

Milling machine table

Locating jig for milling connecting rods. ©

DIAGRAM CR-1.

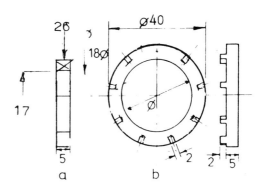

WRIST PIN LOCKING COLLAR.

58

PISTONS

THE PISTONS are of aluminium alloy and may be machined from the solid bar or from castings. If castings are to be used they may be sand cast or cast in a steel die.

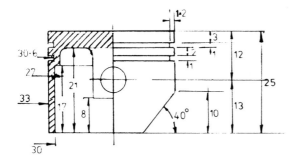

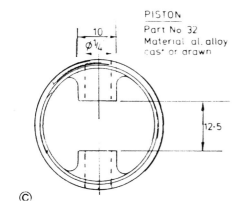

PISTON
Part No 32
Material al. alloy
cast or drawn

PISTON. 32.
Material, Alum. alloy.

Each piston has two piston rings, 1mm square in section. The trailing edge of the skirt of the piston is cut away to clear the adjacent following piston. The gudgeon pins are hollow and hardened and are located end ways by soft alloy end plugs made from aircraft rivets with the heads reduced in diameter. The gudgeon pins are a sliding fit in both the piston and the small end of the connecting rods.

The following description is based on machining the pistons from solid bar. Some of the procedures in the finishing stages apply whichever method is used. A 12" length of 35mm diameter aluminium alloy bar is sufficient to make 10 pistons. The machining is then carried out in the following steps:

1. To begin with both ends must be faced off true.
2. Place the bar on a pair of vee blocks on the milling machine table. Scribe a line across the end and along one side at centre height.
3. Mark out the centres of the gudgeon pin holes along the length of the bar and centre pop each side of the parting line between the pistons.

4. Clamp the bar down on to the vee blocks on the table of the milling machine with the end lines vertical and the centre line on top. The vee blocks must be lined up with the front of the table. Check with a D.T.I. held in the chuck, traversing the table the full length of the work piece.
5. Locate the end gudgeon pin hole with a 'sticky pin'. Centre drill and open out with a 6mm drill without moving the table. Move the table to the next position and repeat on all the gudgeon pin holes. If the spacing of the piston blanks is planned in multiples of the traversing screw pitch they may be spaced out by this means.
6. Chuck the bar in the lathe. Centre and drill out a half inch diameter by 20mm depth (tip of the drill) of the first blank. Bore out 30mm diameter to 8mm depth. All these measurements are made from a setting bar inserted in the gudgeon pin hole. Face the piston skirt to length. Part off the piston blank and repeat along the bar.
7. Make a *milling jig P-1* to hold the blank securely, setting it up to run truly on the rotary table.
8. Mark a line across the diameter of the top of the jig and with the rotary table graduations set at zero. When the piston blank is inserted the skirt projects up 3mm so that the line along the side can be lined up with the line on the jig. This ensures that the gudgeon pin hole is at right angles to the table traverse.

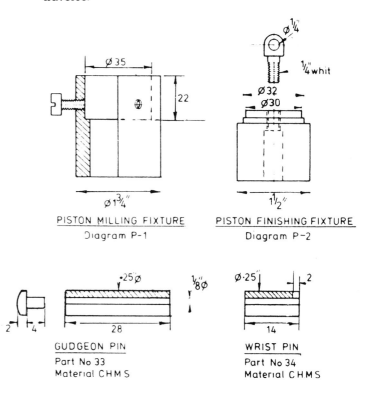

PISTON MILLING FIXTURE
Diagram P-1

PISTON FINISHING FIXTURE
Diagram P-2

GUDGEON PIN
Part No 33
Material CHMS

WRIST PIN
Part No 34
Material CHMS

9. With a half inch end mill, cut the central part of the recess to take the connecting rod little end to a depth of 21mm by a length along the diameter of 28mm over all.

10. With a 3/16" end mill remove all the surplus metal by using rotary table feed with a 45 degree swing either side of the central position. First cut is 8mm depth to 30mm diameter which takes the cut to the level just short of the position of the bottom piston ring. The next cut is taken to 17mm depth to a diameter of 27mm to leave added thickness in the wall to take the pistons rings.

11. Pistons are finished on the finishing jig. *Diagram P-2.* The piston is located by the spigot on the jig engaging the inside of the skirt and drawn down tight by screwing the piston and eye bolt home. The ring grooves are parted in to a depth of 1.2mm. The grooves are to finish 1mm wide.

PISTON RINGS

The rings are made from cast iron bar which is turned .005" over size and bored to size. The rings are then parted off over size in width. They are broken at one point and heat treated for 10 minutes at red heat while clamped between two plates with a wedge 3/16" wide between the ends to spring them out. Some scale will appear which will have to be removed by compressing them into and holding them in the special ring finishing jig. The sides are rubbed down on a lapping plate to fit their individual grooves. While mounted on the finishing jig they should have had the .005" over size skimmed off, sizing them and removing the scale.

INDUCTION SYSTEM

INDUCTION ELBOWS AND PIPES

These are one of the 'difficult' items to produce. Casting by the 'lost wax' method, if the skills and equipment are available, is one alternative.

The method used in this case was to make a steel die as shown in the drawings. This is not so difficult as it seems nor does it take that much more time than making a die for wax patterns. With the number of castings required and the finish obtainable, it makes the production of steel dies well worth while. The induction pipe fittings were cast hollow using plaster cores. The only other casting used on the engine was the oil pump housing and cover plate. This was cast in a steel die with no cores. Once the external shape is produced it is a simple matter in this case to do the necessary machining from the solid for the inside. The dies for casting the plaster cores are made from Marzak which is easily melted and cast and is easily machined.

During development work on the dies the facility with which trials of the dies could be made was of great value as the melts and the results were quick. The dies shown have been proved and should produce good results in aluminium alloy. The cores for the outer fitting can be dispensed with and cast solid. It is possible to hollow them out by drilling etc.

The inside finish of the dies is important and 'draw' must be built in to allow the castings to be removed. The dies should be coated with some mould coating.

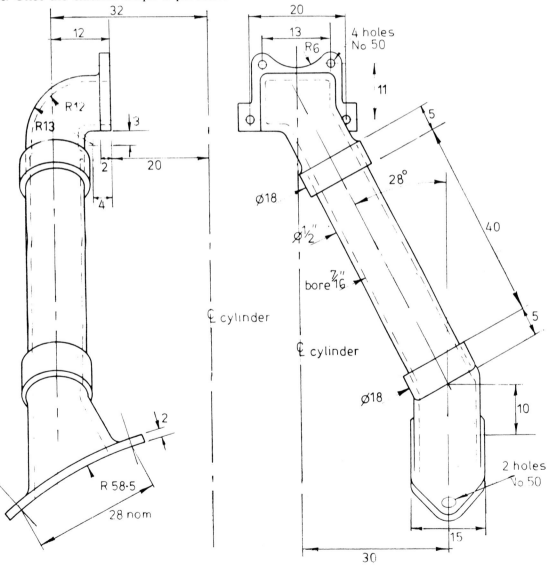

INDUCTION PIPE & ELBOWS. 17.
Material, Alum. alloy.

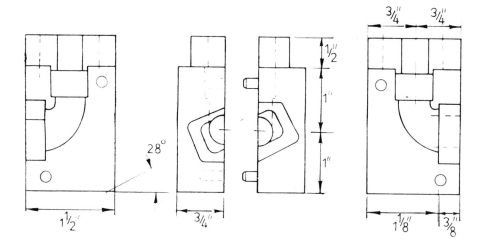

DIE FOR CASTING INDUCTION PIPE ELBOWS.
Diagram IP-1. Material, mild steel.

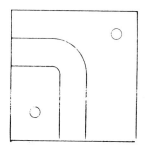
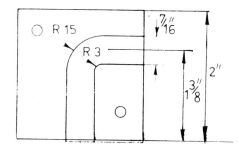

The steel die with a plaster core installed for casting the outer induction pipe elbows.

Locating pins having a tapered end should be provided as the dies need to be quickly reassembled while still hot. Dies should be pre-heated before casting is started. Casting metal temperature is important.

The Marzak dies for producing the plaster cores are coated with some proprietary mould release before assembly and having the plaster poured in. After a short time they may be separated, the cores removed and

The steel dies set up for casting with the plaster core in place.

thoroughly dried out. The plaster cores as they come out of the dies must be cleaned up and modified where necessary. It is simpler to produce a straight forward die which produces cores of a round section. These are

The casting as it leaves the dies, which are shown on either side.

In the case of the inner fitting a special machining fixture is required to hold it at the required angle. This fixture is shown on the accompanying drawing. The block may be made of any suitable material. Marzak is particularly suitable being easily cast to the approximate shape and finished. It possesses adequate strength for the job.

The blanks firstly need to have the 58.5mm radius 'xx', finished. They can then be clamped onto the block and held firmly by means of dogs and screws. The block is profiled to accept them and tilted to the required angle of 28 degrees. The screws which secure the block between the lugs on the base plate at either end are then tightened securely. The boss is centralised and the base plate is secured to the face plate in the correct position to machine the induction pipe socket.

The bolt holes which are used to secure these fittings to the distribution box are set out from reference to the holes tapped in the outer diameter of the thrust box. Due to the angular disposition of these, studs cannot be used for both. One stud and one hexagon headed screw can be used or two hexagon headed screws to allow assembly. Hollowing out the inside is

The inner induction pipe fitting set up on the special machining fixture for machining the induction pipe socket and some of the bore.

quickly pared down to the desired shape of the core. This is more practical than producing some odd shaped hole in a piece of metal. The outer induction elbow cores need to have flats made on the port end to conform to the rectangular shape at the junction with the cylinder head. This is easily done with a knife. Trial castings will show where further work is required if the fitting is sawed through.

MACHINING THE FITTINGS

The outer fittings can be set up on an ordinary angle plate with the boss centered as shown in the accompanying photograph. Locating strips can be attached to the angle plate to locate them in the same position each time.

rather an ad hoc process, using drills, burrs and scrapers until a reasonable opening is produced. External finishing is done with files and emery cloth.

INDUCTION PIPES

The induction pipes are a half inch O.D. aluminium alloy tube. Thin tube was not available so a 7/16" drill was run through the lengths before parting off. The pipes are sealed into the end fitting with a silicon sealer used in the automotive industry which is resistant to petrol.

Three stages in the production of the inner induction pipe fittings.

The induction elbow casting after being cut off from its header, mounted on an angle plate for boring the induction pipe socket.

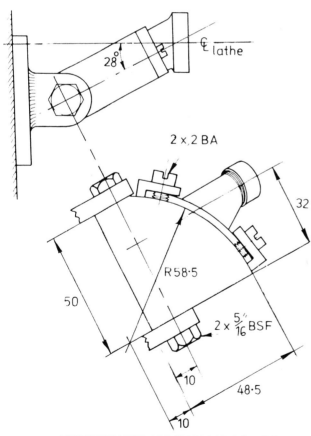

FIXTURE FOR MACHINING LOWER INDUCTION PIPE ELBOWS.

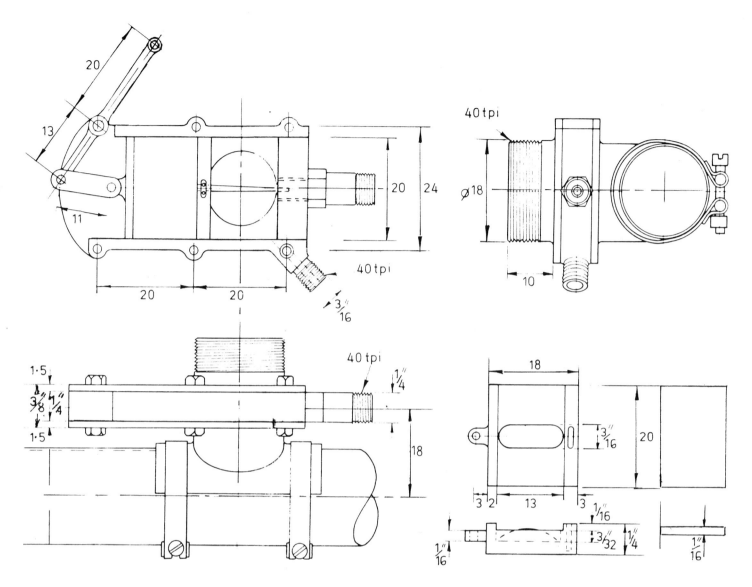

CARBURETTOR. 43.

THROTTLE SLIDE.
Material, brass.

CARBURETTOR

The carburettor is known as a 'bloctube' type and is particularly simple. It is gravity fed. There is no float chamber and when the fuel is turned on it is free to flow through the jet subject only to the restriction by the fuel metering needle. For this reason the fuel is only turned on at the fuel cock when the engine is being primed for starting and when it is actually running.

The carburettor consists of a short extension screwed to the rear end of crankshaft. This carries a slide box which houses the jet and throttle slide, which constitute the vital parts of the carburettor. The throttle slide has one spring loaded side which holds the main part of the throttle in contact with the housing to prevent an excess of unwanted air being drawn in. The slide should be a good fit in the upper and lower parts of the housing for the same reason.

The fuel jet projects horizontally at right angles to the tubular body of the carburettor, and is immediately opposite the throttle slide. A tapered needle is mounted in the end of the throttle slide in line with the jet. As the throttle moves this metering needle moves with it, thus varying its effective aperture. Air is induced through each end of the cross tube at the rear of the engine. In the full size engine this tube was extended through each side of the fuselage. In addition to providing an unrestricted air supply this feature would allow the flame from a backfire to be discharged clear of the aircraft. This cross tube is attached to the lugs on the rear of the carburettor body by two clamps.

The tapered needle is held in a socket in the end of the throttle slide by a small circlip engaging in an annular groove machined in it. It must be capable of limited movement to allow it to slide freely in the jet

65

which it closely fills when the throttle is shut. The metering taper on the jet is a flat filed along one side. This allows simple modification when tuning the engine by simply increasing or decreasing the degree of taper. It also provides a jet orifice which is not so liable to block up as if it was diametrically tapered and had an annular orifice.

The carburettor is made up from brass. The front and back plates are cut out together from 1/16" thick hard brass sheet. The short extension which forms the attachment to the rear end of the crankshaft is silver soldered to the front plate. The saddle fitting which holds the cross tube is built up and silver soldered to the rear plate.

The central portion is built up from quarter inch thick brass which is soft soldered to the front plate. The holes for the bolts are drilled with all held together. The whole assembly is then finished externally. The bolt hole at the bottom, below the jet, is drilled 3/32" diameter to allow any excess fuel to drain around the bolt and down to the drain union. The bolt which forms the pivot for the throttle lever has a plain 3/32" diameter between the plates. A shoulder bears against the front plate and a nut holds it secure.

The throttle slide is made a close sliding fit. The centre of the side away from the engine is milled out to take the loose piece which is spring-loaded by a flat spring in the recess. This is to give the slide action a certain amount of stiffness and to prevent as far as possible excess air entering.

The metering needle is 1/16" diameter and the hole in the throttle slide into which it is anchored must allow it to align itself with the jet. It can be marked out through the jet with the carburettor assembly. A slot is cut in the jet side of the slide to take a retaining circlip which holds the needle captive. This slot must not be cut right through the front side of the slide.

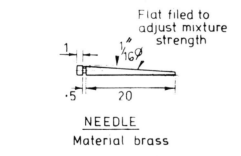

NEEDLE
Material brass

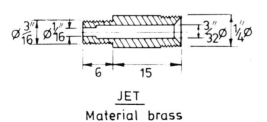

JET
Material brass

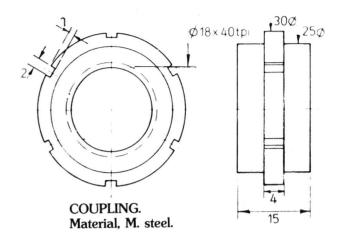

COUPLING.
Material, M. steel.

FUEL & OIL TANK

The combined fuel and oil tank is made from .015" thick hard brass sheet. The outer wrapper is first made with a folded longitudinal seam. To form the ends a piece of stock bar is turned so that it will just enter the tube. This is then measured and a further .030" is removed from the outer diameter. The end is then slightly domed to form the die. A piece of tube is then bored out to the previously determined inside diameter of the wrapper. Three discs of brass .015" thick are then annealed, dished and flanged by pressing between the dies which are forced between the jaws of a vice. Holes for the combined filler outlet fittings are made. The whole assembly is then soft soldered together.

A small stop cock is screwed into the oil outlet. The petrol control valve serves a dual purpose in shutting off the petrol and also controlling the flow which will be found to be necessary with the tank mounted where it is shown. It will be found that the mixture strength varies quite noticeably from the full tank to empty. It is also necessary with the type of carburettor used, that fuel flow needs to be adjusted to secure smooth idling. This was the case in the full size engine where a separate mixture control was provided and which required frequent adjustment.

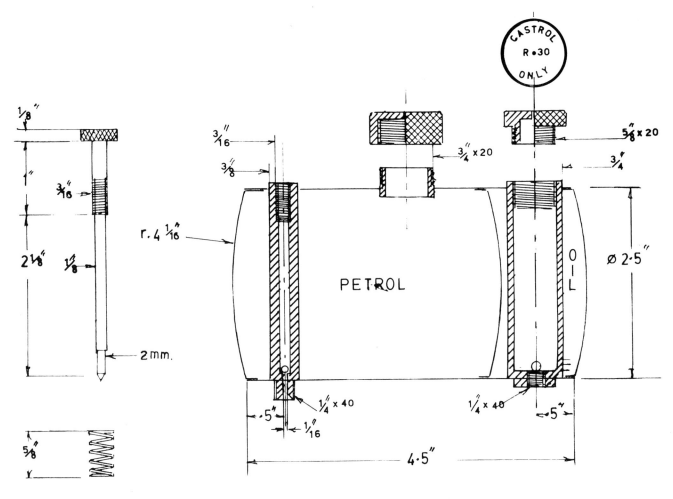

FUEL & OIL TANK.
Material. brass.

The quarter scale B.R.2.

LUBRICATION

LUBRICATING OIL SYSTEM

This is a total loss system. The oil pump is mounted on the back of the central support and driven by a 24-tooth gear meshing with the 54-tooth gear on the thrust box. It is geared down by means of a worm and wheel inside the pump casing, with a ratio of 30 to 1, giving an overall ratio of 13.3 to 1. The worm wheel shaft is formed with a crank which actuates the pump plunger and oscillates the pump cylinder about its trunnions. The cylinder bears on the port face by the action of a spring in the trunnion on the opposite side. As the cylinder oscillates the inlet and delivery ports are uncovered and covered alternately in time with the action of the plunger. The inlet port leads to the pump outlet and check valve. All pipe unions on the pressure side are 3/16" x 40 T.P.I. The oil from the tank is led by gravity to the bottom of the pump casing.

The oil pump and cover is made from a die casting of either Marzak or aluminium alloy as shown in the

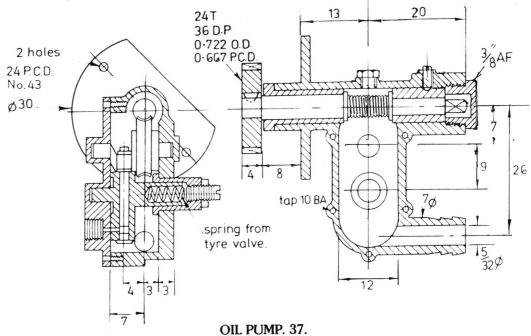

OIL PUMP. 37.
Material, Al. alloy or Mazak.

COVER.
Material, Al. alloy or Mazak.

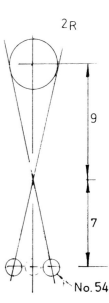

PORT LAYOUT.

photographs and machined in accordance with the drawings. The construction is fairly straightforward.

The worm gear is produced by setting up a blank free to rotate on a bolt on a piece of steel held in the lathe tool post. A 3/16" x 24 T.P.I. taper tap is chucked in the lathe, supported by the tailstock centre either male or female according to the tap. With the lathe rotating slowly the blank is fed in to the tap and then axially along it until it begins to turn. It is then slowly fed along until the full depth is being cut by the tap. There is no need to pre-gash the blank. This should result in a 30-tooth worm wheel.

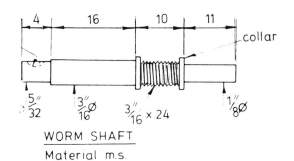

WORM SHAFT
Material m.s.

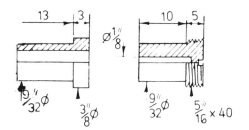

WORM SHAFT BUSHES
Material ph.B

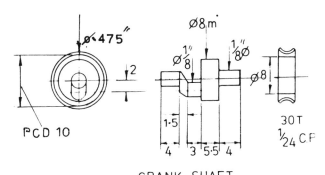

CRANK SHAFT
Material m.s.

The dies used for casting the oil pump body.

The port layout is most important and is best achieved by making a simple drilling jig which is used for both the pump barrel and the port face by turning it over. On the delivery stroke the oil is forced under pressure past the ball check valve, into the engine lubricating system. One oil pipe leads from the check valve to the connection on the rear of the central support, from where it is forced along the 1/16" O.D. stainless steel pipe inside the crankshaft. The other goes to the pulsometer.

THE PULSOMETER provides a visual indication that the lubrication system is functioning. In the full size engine the surface of the oil in the pulsometer could be seen pulsating. This is not apparent in the quarter scale engine, probably due to scale effect. However the oil builds about half way up the glass where the system appears to reach a state of balance and does provide the visual evidence required. When the engine is stopped the oil level returns to the bottom of the glass.

Machining the oil pump casting on an angle plate.

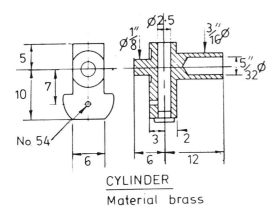

CYLINDER
Material brass

Due to the fact that the fuel/air mixture is ingested up the hollow crankshaft and through the moving parts in the crankcase on its way to the cylinders it is absolutely vital that the oil used is not soluble in the fuel and thus washed off the parts requiring lubrication. For this reason castor oil was used as a lubricant and Castrol R30 has proved satisfactory in this engine provided that straight petrol is used, preferably lead-free and most certainly not containing any methanol.

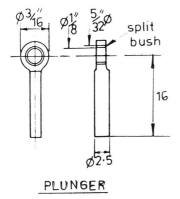

PLUNGER

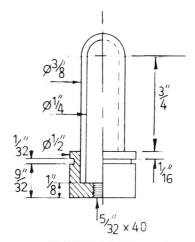

PULSOMETER.
Material, glass & brass.

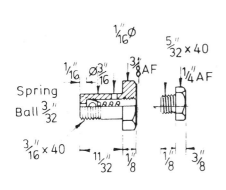

NON RETURN VALVE
Material brass

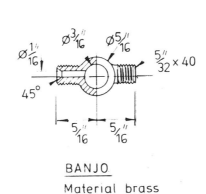

BANJO
Material brass

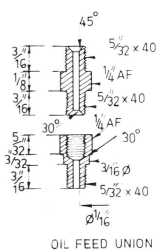

OIL FEED UNION
Material brass

Close up of the rear end showing the accessories.

The battery pack and coil mounted in a convenient box.

IGNITION SYSTEM

TYPE

Dual ignition systems are fitted. Scale effect prevents, so far, a working magneto in this scale. Ignition is therefore by a 12V coil which is switched in the usual way by contact breakers which are made to resemble scale magnetos.

The contact breakers give two sparks per revolution and run at two and a quarter times engine speed, each giving nine sparks every two revolutions of the engine. The firing order is 1,3,5,7,0,2,4,6,8.

CONTACT BREAKERS are of the axial contact type and were designed to meet certain requirements. The points had to be readily accessible for cleaning and adjusting. In addition the main contact assembly can be freed by slackening the four screws at the contact breaker end, allowing the assembly to be rotated and the ignition timing accurately set.

The contacts were salvaged from a discarded domestic dish-washing machine which has numbers of

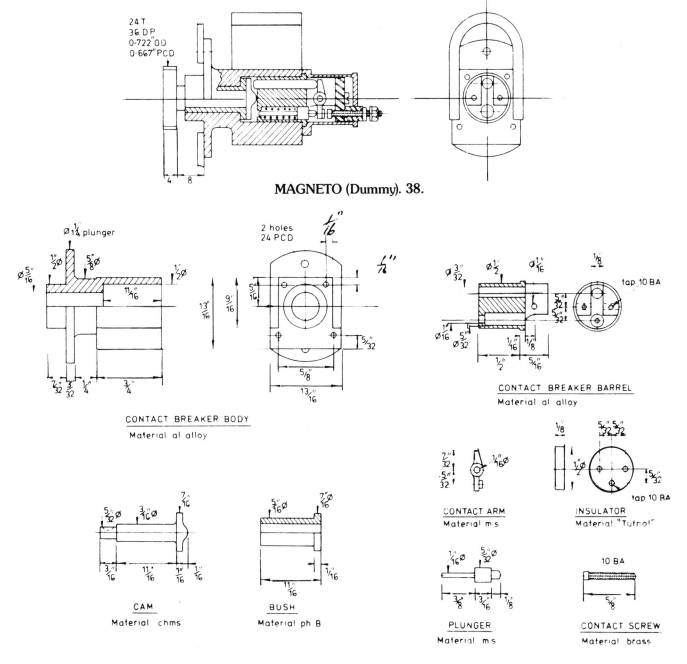

MAGNETO (Dummy). 38.

CONTACT BREAKER BODY
Material al alloy

CONTACT BREAKER BARREL
Material al alloy

CONTACT ARM
Material m s

INSULATOR
Material "Tufnol"

CAM
Material chms

BUSH
Material ph B

PLUNGER
Material m s

CONTACT SCREW
Material brass

contacts about 3/16" diameter in its control box. They were cut off the brass strip through which they were rivetted. They are then soldered contact face to a piece of quarter inch diameter brass rod. This is then chucked and the contact point turned down to the required diameter. At the same time the small shank is turned which locates the contact point in the rocker for one and on the head of the adjustable contact screw for the other. The contact point is now placed in its position with flux and the brass rod heated up which at the same time solders the contact point into its seating and frees the brass rod. The job is completed by cleaning the contact face of the point.

The contact screw is screwed into the insulated part of the contact breaker assembly. The thread in the insulator is only started into the insulated material, leaving the rest of the thread to be formed by forcing a 10BA screw through without removing any further material. This is so that the adjustment screw will be self-locking and retain its adjustment.

The push rod which operates the rocker is nylon.

Looking from the rear the right hand contact breaker supplies the front set of spark plugs and the left hand one the rear spark plugs. Two coils are necessary. The high tension current is fed to insulated terminals on the Central Support. The current jumps the air gap to the ring of contacts on the distributor disc. This arrangement of having an external spark gap has been found to be very effective in cases where spark plugs tend to oil up and provide a low resistance path for the current to leak before the voltage builds up. The external gap forms a barrier until the voltage builds up to a value which is sufficient to jump this gap.

The terminal lugs on the contact segments are connected to the appropriate spark plugs with thin bare wire which is passed through the insulated fair leads held in clips secured under the screws which hold the

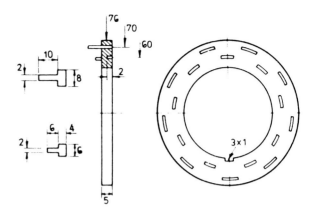

DISTRIBUTOR DISC. 40.
Material "Tufnol", etc.

rear cover on the distribution box. On the full size engine the wires were bare to reduce windage. If desired, thin insulated wire could be used but, here again, is a departure from full size practice. It has been noticed that there is some sparking over taking place under humid conditions or when the engine is first started. This usually clears and does not appear to affect the running to any great extent once the engine has warmed up.

THE DISTRIBUTOR DISC is made from some rigid insulating board 5mm thick. A 4" square blank 5mm thick is chucked in the 4 jaw. The centre is bored out to fit the spigot on the rear of the thrust box. Two annular grooves are turned in the face of the disc 2mm deep as shown in the drawing. Two rows of 9 holes in each are drilled from the bottom of the grooves right through the disc to take the shanks of the contact pieces.

The disc is then parted off to 76mm diameter.

The 'T' shaped contacts are formed to the radius of the grooves. The contacts are inserted loosely into the circular groove with the stem of the 'T' through the holes, the longer stems being in the outer row. Mix a batch of Araldite, (not the quick setting kind as time is required to set all the contacts in place.) Fill the grooves and seat the contacts firmly home in position. The Araldite must fill the grooves between the contacts up to the level of the insulation material. The faces of the contact pieces should be projecting above the surface. When the Araldite has completely set any surplus may be cleaned off and the key-way cut in the bore.

The disc is then chucked so that it runs truly and the contact faces are very carefully faced off just proud of the insulated disc.

Dual ignition was installed to maintain scale. However for demonstration running this is not necessary and the engine runs very well with just one of the systems functioning.

Component parts of the 'magneto' contact breaker and the 24 tooth driving gear.

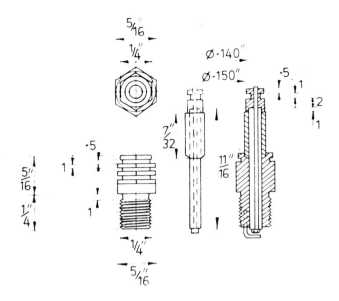

SPARK PLUG. 42.
Material M. steel & ceramic.

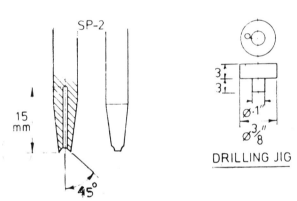

SP-2

DRILLING JIG

SPARK PLUGS

Machine the spark plug bodies from 5/16" A.F. mild steel. Chuck and complete the machining as shown in the drawings and cut off. When all the bodies are finished to this stage they can be held in a screwed bush and the top end faced and the hole drilled and counter bored for the Teflon sleeve which goes over the upper part of the insulator.

Both the earth electrode and the central electrode are nichrome wire 0.035" thick. This was obtained from a heavy duty heater element and has proved ideal for the job as it is not subject to corrosion. It is soft enough to accept the swaging indentations in the earth electrode and also can be formed into a head for the central electrode.

A drilling jig must be made to drill the holes for the earth electrodes as shown in *Diagram SP/1.*

A swaging tool must also be made as shown in Diagram SP/2. This is turned and drilled 0.040" to a depth of 15mm. The hole is counter sunk 45 degrees. The tool is then hardened and tempered, after which

each side of the tip is carefully removed with an oil stone to form the two swaging points.

Drill the earth electrode hole through the drilling jig 3mm deep. Install the earth electrodes which are 10mm length of 0.035" nichrome wire. These are secured in the plug body by passing the swaging tool over the electrode and giving it a light tap which closes a small area of metal on either side of the electrodes, securing it in the spark plug body.

Cut off lengths of ceramic tube 24mm long and square the ends to length with a diamond file. The method used for cutting the ceramic tube was by scoring a mark around the circumference with a diamond.

Cut off and form heads on 35mm lengths of .035" nichrome wire. Tin the outer ends. It was found that this could be done by using killed spirits. Install these in the ceramic insulators with Loctite. Solder the terminal ends on to the central electrodes and cut off the surplus length. The ceramic tube is 2.5mm O.D. x 1mm bore.

Make Teflon sleeves and fit over the ceramic insulators in contact with the terminal ends.

Install the complete insulator and central electrode assembly into the body shell with Loctite.

The final job is to bend the earth electrode over to form the spark gap. The wire is then cut off to length with a shear type tool which leaves a square end on the wire.

Copper washers are parted off .5mm long from quarter inch I.D. copper tube and annealed before use.

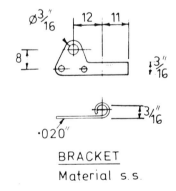

BRACKET
Material s.s.

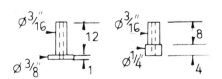

IGNITION LEAD BUSHES.
Part No 41
Material "Tufnol"

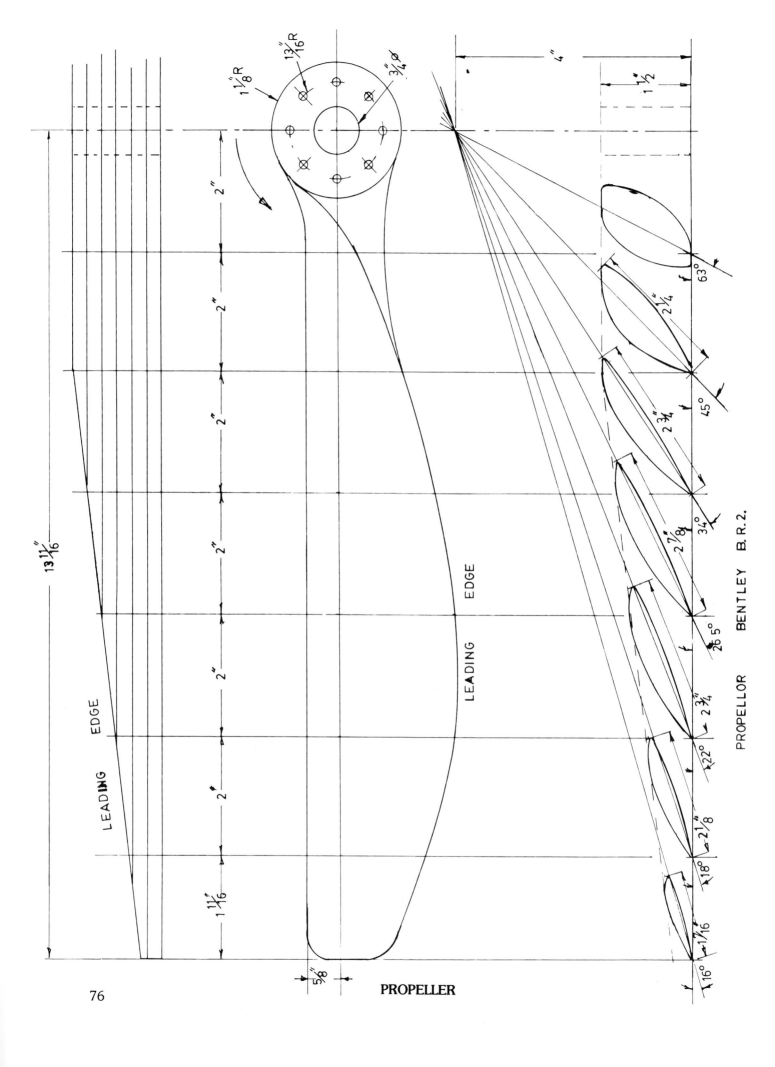

PROPELLER

PROPELLOR   BENTLEY   B.R.2.

76

PROPELLER

TIMBER SELECTION

The timber selected is most important but will depend on what is available in the country. It must possess a fine grain so that a good finish may be achieved and high strength. It must be highly resistant to splitting and have a straight grain. It must have the capacity to be carved in any direction without the grain lifting. One book published in the wooden propeller era states that walnut is probably the best all round wood. Birch is tougher. Mahogany is lighter. The writer has no experience as to how these woods carve. The wood used in this case came from New Guinea.

Some propellers have been seen with very contrasting timber alternating as laminations to produce a visual effect. This is not recommended because the propeller is a highly stressed item and greatest strength lies in bonding laminations that are as compatible as possible. It must be remembered that this engine has a total displaced volume of 350cc and is therefore capable of producing considerable power.

CONSTRUCTION

The timber is required in quarter inch x 3" finished section dressed all round. Each alternate lamination must be end for end to ensure the maximum strength and density. Disposing the laminations in this manner also helps to balance the propeller.

The prepared laminations should not be sanded. The finish straight off the planer provides the best gluing surface. They are evenly coated with Aquadhere P.V.A. wood working glue, placed together and clamped between two heavy, straight lengths of timber. The clamps should not be further apart than 5" to 6". It will assist in keeping them in alignment if a 1/8" hole is drilled through the centre. A piece of 1/8" brass rod will keep them in position while the glue is setting. It can later be punched out and the hole then used to pilot the drill through for the propeller shaft hole. Enough glue should be used to ensure complete coverage and should exude freely out of all joints. The clamping pressure should be even. After about five minutes it will be found that the clamps can be taken up further. After setting and curing is complete which takes 12 hours, the clamps are removed and the blade outline is drawn on and the outline cut out. The endwise tapers on the front of the blades are cut. The hole is drilled out 3/4" diameter for the propeller shaft.

The blank is held for carving by a bolt with a large washer holding it down on to a piece of timber held in the vice. This must have a plane upper surface which forms the reference surface for the templates which govern the blade angles and profiles at the various stations. These are clearly marked on the reference surface.

The carving can now be carried out to the drawing using Surform tools both flat and convex face. When the final shape is being approached the finishing stages can be done with a spokeshave, scrapers and successively finer grades of abrasive paper.

Checks must be made during these stages of the balance and corrections made. These checks are made by passing a close fitting mandrel through the propeller shaft hole. This is rested on true and level parallel straight edges. Care must be taken that draughts are excluded.

When the final finish and balance is achieved the eight propeller bolt holes are drilled 9/64" diameter.

The finish is a clear gloss Estapol which shows up the grain of the wood and the laminations which results in a pleasing appearance. Three coats at least will be necessary with sanding each time using fine sandpaper. After each coat and sanding it is necessary to try for balance and correct by applying a more liberal coat to the lighter blade or in an extreme case an additional coat.

The propeller

A replica Sopwith Snipe built by Col Palen, in flight over Old Rhineback aerodrome.

STARTING THE ENGINE

When the engine is finally assembled it will be found to be extremely stiff. this is largely due to the friction of the 18 piston rings. It was found necessary to 'motor' the engine by rigging up a driving arrangement. This was done with the spark plugs removed. After 8 hours the engine had freed up enough to start. Short runs were gradually extended in duration, governed by the degree to which it heated up.

Starting procedure involves initial priming by giving two or four complete revolutions of the engine with the fuel cock turned on and the throttle set 1/16" open. The fuel is then immediately turned off to prevent flooding. A further couple of turns are given to distribute the mixture. The propeller is then set to a convenient position to pull through for starting. The ignition is now switched on and the engine started. Immediately it fires the fuel is turned on and the performance regulated by the throttle and the mixture control on the petrol supply.

On every occasion before starting check that the engine is securely bolted down and that the propeller bolts are secure. Also that there is ample clearance for the propeller to turn and that there are no loose objects, rags etc. which can be drawn in by the propeller as there is a substantial inflow of air.

Most importantly the propeller must always be treated as live. Bystanders or observers must be thoroughly briefed that this is the case and that the propeller cannot be seen when it is running and to keep well clear. A hit will have serious consequences.

Due to the fact that the engine will be stopped by turning off the fuel it is important to immediately turn off the ignition when it has stopped.

The best place to stand for running it is behind the engine and to the right hand side. If the propeller is set after the initial priming is completed in a position approaching the vertical it can be conveniently pulled over to start immediately the ignition has been switched on – 'contact'. To observe aircraft practice switches are arranged to be 'up' – pointing to the sky – when on!

There is a common conception that the rotary engines spray castor oil all over the place. This is to some extent true, however the greater part of it is deflected down when the exhaust valves open approaching bottom dead centre. This is helped by the resultant slip stream.

The model B.R.2 running.

Snipe 7F.1

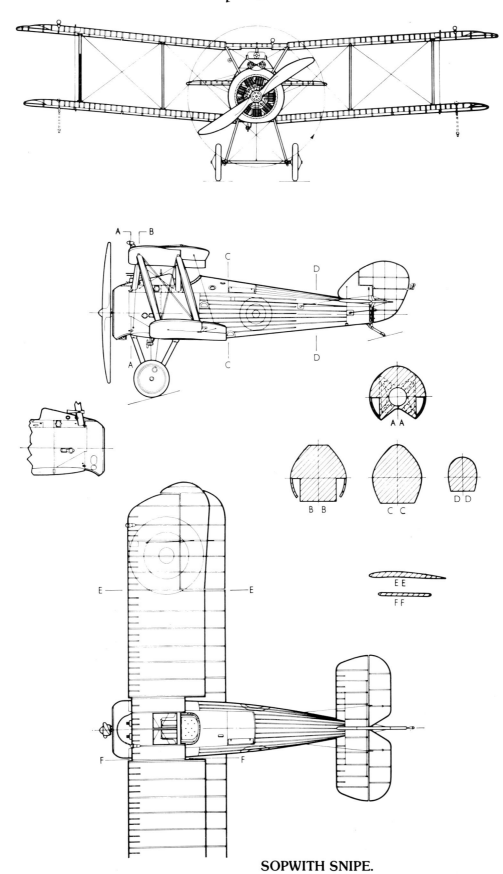

A B
C
D
A A
B B
C C
D D
E E
F F
E E
F F

SOPWITH SNIPE.

APPENDIX

Reproduced by kind permission of the Ministry of Defence.

FOR OFFICIAL USE.

AIR PUBLICATION 359.

(3rd Edition. January, 1925.)

B.R.2 AERO ENGINE.

This descriptive handbook on the B.R.2 aero engine is issued for the information and guidance of all concerned.

By Command of the Air Council,

W7 Nicholas

AIR MINISTRY,

May, 1925.

LONDON:

PUBLISHED BY HIS MAJESTY'S STATIONERY OFFICE.

To be purchased directly from H.M. STATIONERY OFFICE at the following addresses :
Adastral House, Kingsway, London, W.C. 2; 28, Abingdon Street, London, S.W. 1;
York Street, Manchester; 1, St. Andrew's Crescent, Cardiff;
or 120, George Street, Edinburgh;
or through any Bookseller.

1925.

Price 2s. Net.

LEADING PARTICULARS.

Make of engine and rated H.P.	B.R.2. 200 H.P.
Number and arrangement of cylinders	9 Rotary radial.
Bore - - - - - -	140 mm. 5·51 in.
Stroke - - - - -	180 mm. 7·09 in.
Stroke volume of one cylinder - -	2770·88 c.c. 169 cub. in.
Total stroke volume of engine -	24,937·92 c.c. 1521 cub. in.
Area of one piston - - -	153·93 sq. cm. 23·86 sq. in.
Total piston area of engine -	1385·44 sq. cm. 214·56 sq.in.
Clearance volume of one cylinder -	692·72 c.c. 42·25 cub. in.
Compression ratio - - -	5 : 1
Normal B.H.P. and speed - -	238 at 1300 R.P.M.
Piston speed - - - -	1536 FT./MIN. at 1300 R.P.M.
	1593 ,, ,, 1350 ,,
Brake mean effective pressure -	At Normal R.P.M.
	95·2 lb/sq. in.
Stroke volume per B.H.P. -	6·39 cub. in.
Piston area per B.H.P. - -	·9016 sq. in.
H.P. per cub. ft. of stroke volume	271.
H.P. per sq. ft. of piston area	159·7.
Direction of rotation of airscrew	Right hand tractor.
Normal speed of airscrew - -	Engine speed.
Lubrication system - -	Le Rhone Type Plunger Pump.
Brand of oil recommended	Pharmaceutical Castor.
Oil consumption per hour - -	18 pints.
Oil consumption per B.H.P. hour	·0756 pints.
Type of carburetter - - -	Bloctube.
Fuel consumption per hour -	138 pints.
Fuel consumption per B.H.P. hour -	·58 pints.
Type of magneto - - -	Two A.D.S or P.L.R.
Firing sequence of engine - -	1, 3, 5, 7, 0, 2, 4, 6, 8.
Numbering of cylinders - -	1, 2, 3, 4, 5, 6, 7, 8, 0.
Speed of magneto - - -	2¼ times engine speed.
Direction of rotation of magneto, facing driving end of armature.	Clockwise.
Magneto timing - - -	20°–26° early (23° desired).
Sparking plugs - - -	K.L.G. F. 9.
Inlet valve opens. Degrees on crank	0° before T.D.C. ± ·5°
Inlet valve closes. Degrees on crank	58° After B.D.C. ± ·5°
Maximum lift of inlet valve -	12 mm., approximately.
Smallest Dia. of inlet - -	52 mm.
Exhaust valve opens. Degrees on crank.	72° before B.D.C. ± ·5°
Exhaust valve closes. Degrees on crank.	10° after T.D.C. ± ·5°.
Maximum lift of exhaust valve -	13·5 mm., approximately.
Smallest diameter of exhaust -	58 mm.
Direction of rotation of revolution counter drive, facing driving shaft on engine.	Anticlockwise.
Weight of engine dry - -	500 lb.
Weight per B.H.P. Dry - -	2·1 lb.
Weight of fuel per hour - -	124 lb.
Weight of oil per hour - -	22 lb.
Total weight of fuel and oil per hour	146 lb.

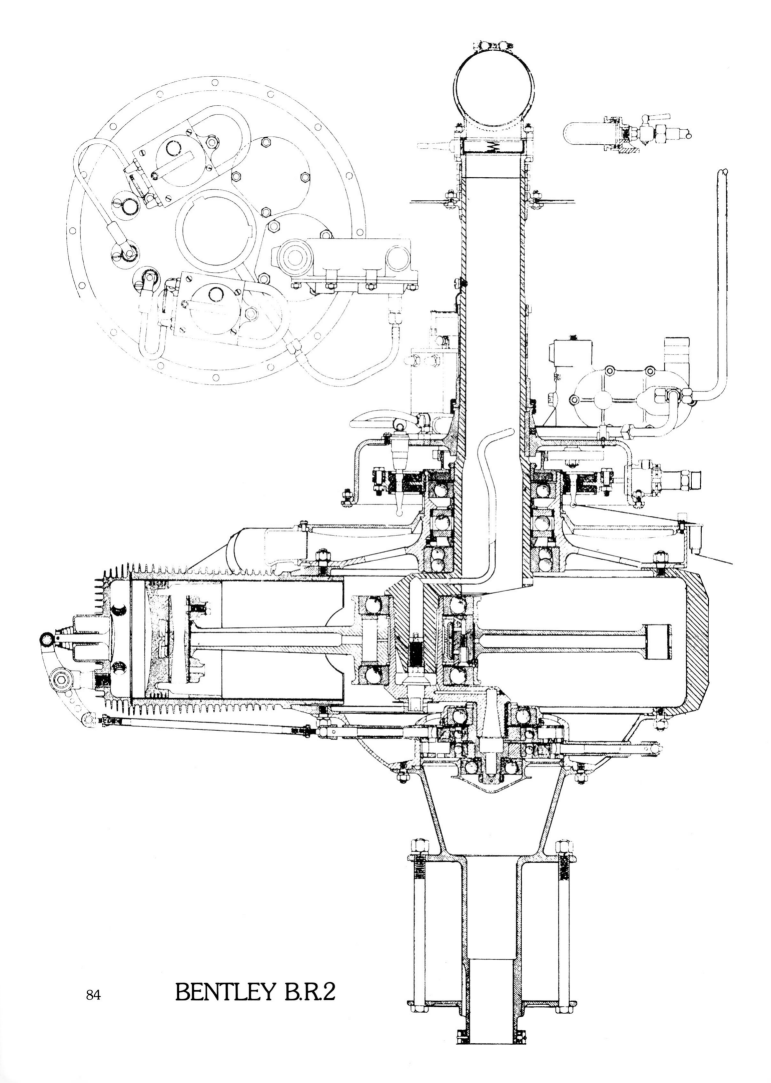

84   BENTLEY B.R.2

CHAPTER I.—GENERAL DESCRIPTION.

(*Note.*—The airscrew end of the engine is termed the FRONT in all the following descriptions and instructions.)

Crankshaft.

1.—(i) The crankshaft is built up of three pieces as shown in fig. 1, viz. :—

    (*a*) The long end, or long or main crank.
    (*b*) The short crank, or maneton.
    (*c*) The extension shaft, or cam gear shaft.

(ii) The joint between A and B forms the crankpin, the male taper of A being pulled into the female taper in B by the maneton screw. The taper joint is located by a long key and the screw is then locked by a washer which threads over the square head of the screw and over two small pegs fixed in the front crankpin web. Split pins are then passed through holes in the pegs, and prevent the washer from coming off. The extension shaft C is pushed into place over the front end of the maneton B, on which it is located by a key, and is prevented from coming off by the construction of the cam gear box (fig. 37).

2. As is normal in rotary engines, the crankshaft is rigidly mounted in its supports, and serves the following purposes ·—

    (i) It forms a means of attaching the engine to the aircraft.
    (ii) The explosive mixture is drawn from the carburetter into the crankcase along the hollow centre of the crankshaft.
    (iii) The oil delivery pipe runs inside the crankshaft.
    (iv) The crankshaft forms the spindle on which the rotating parts of the engine revolve.
    (v) The crankpin is the fixed point against which the force of the explosion acts.

3. The above points may now be studied in detail. The crankshaft is mounted in two supports as shown in fig. 2, D being the central support and E the rear support. Both supports are bolted to suitable plates in the fuselage of the aircraft. The central support takes the weight of the engine, holds the crankshaft in alignment by means of a taper joint and two keys, and carries a number of fittings including the magnetos and pumps. The rear support steadies the engine and transfers the pull of the airscrew to the aircraft.

4. The details of the crankshaft attachment to the central support are illustrated in fig. 3. The central support is a

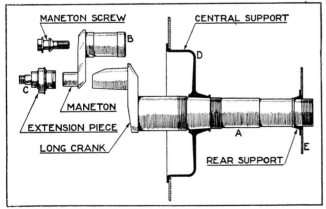

FIG. 2.—CRANKSHAFT (DISMANTLED) AND SUPPORTS.

steel disc bolted to a ring bearer plate in the fuselage. At its centre is a tapered boss into which the crankshaft is entered from the front. A pair of keys and keyways fix the crankshaft in this boss and also position it so that the crank is vertical.

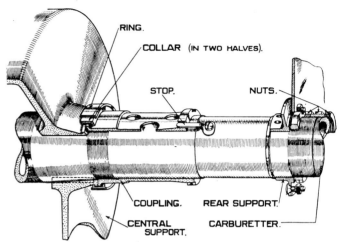

FIG. 3.—DETAILS OF CRANKSHAFT MOUNTING AND COUPLING.

An internal thread (right hand) on the coupling engages with the external thread on the crankshaft. When the engine is being erected, this coupling obtains a purchase on the central support by means of the two flanges, one on the coupling and the other on the support, which are linked together by the half collars and their ring. The coupling, as it is screwed home, pulls the crankshaft up into the taper boss. Similarly in dismantling the engine, the unscrewing of the coupling pushes the crankshaft out of the taper sleeve.

5. The rear end of the crankshaft protrudes through the rear support, behind which it is secured by a ring nut; the carburetter is then attached by three ring nuts to the rear extremity of the long crank. The mixture is sucked along the hollow straight portion of the long crank and passes into the crankcase through the orifice at the foot of the rear crankpin web. Fig. 25 shows that the oil pump feeds oil through an external pipe to a hole drilled in the long end of the crankshaft; from this point a copper pipe inside the crankshaft conveys the oil to a duct drilled up the rear crank web.

6. The forward extremity of the long crank forms the inner part of the crankpin, and is cut away in front, as shown in Fig. 1, to facilitate threading the master connecting rod into position when erecting the engine. The maneton forms the outer portion of the crankpin. The male taper of the inner crankpin is forcibly drawn into the female taper of the maneton by means of the maneton plug. A duct drilled down the centre of the front crank web supplies oil for the lubrication of the cam gears.

Crankshaft bearings.

7. There are four main ball bearings on the crankshaft. Two support the thrust box, and two the cam gear box. Two ball bearings, of much smaller dimensions, carry the inlet and exhaust cam gear. The master rod assembly is supported on two large ball bearings and a ball thrust is fitted in the thrust box.

Crankcase.

8. The crankcase consists of three main portions :—

    (i) The crankcase proper. The cylinders are spigoted into apertures disposed radially round its periphery, and are held in position on it by long bolts.
    (ii) The cam gear box, which is bolted to the front face of the crankcase. (The nose piece, made in one with the airscrew hub, bolts on to the front of the cam gear box).

(iii) The thrust box, which is bolted to the rear face of the crankcase. An aluminium plate covers a circular recess in the rear of the thrust box, and so provides a gas chamber.

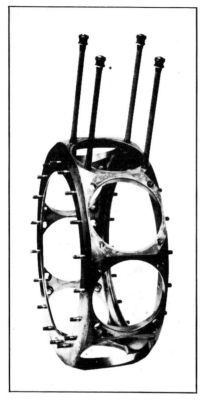

Fig. 4.—Crankcase, with one Set of Cylinder holding down Bolts.

Cylinders.

9. The cylinder barrels are of cast aluminium, shrunk on to steel liners. The lower end of the barrel is formed with a spigot, which fits loosely into the crankcase, to allow for expansion during running. The spigot protrudes about two inches into the crankcase and is drilled with holes which act as vents for oil flung by centrifugal force into the outer corners of the crankcase. The cylinder spigot is cut away at both leading and trailing edges to allow clearance for the connecting rods. Above the spigot is an external flange which beds down on to the face of the crankcase. There are 22 radiating fins cast upon the barrel, and they increase gradually in depth from the base towards the head. The cylinders are numbered 1, 2, 3, 4, 5, 6, 7, 8, 0, the number 9 being avoided for fear of confusion with 6 when the digits are inverted. The cylinders are numbered in a clockwise direction, when viewed from the front.

Cylinder heads.

10. The cylinder heads are of steel, and are formed with five circumferential radiating fins which are bevelled off at both front and rear of the heads. Induction valve boxes are machined in one piece with the heads, and have steel guides pressed into them. Tripod exhaust valve cages are similarly machined in one with the heads, but the guides are cast iron. Short steel brackets screwed into the heads support the valve rockers. Two sparking plug bosses are provided in the leading face of each head. The cylinder heads and cylinders are attached to the crankcase by four long bolts to each cylinder, the joint between the head and cylinder being of

Fig. 5.—Cylinder.

the plain ground type. The four bolts are equally spaced around the cylinder, the cooling fins being recessed to allow 1 mm. clearance round the bolts. These bolts are inserted from inside the crankcase, their heads being slotted to take a screwdriver. Castellated nuts screw on to the outer ends of the holding down bolts and are locked by split pins. The bolts should not be disturbed except when replacement is necessary, as their removal tends to destroy their close fit in the crankcase.

Fig. 6.—Cylinder, with the Head dismounted.

86

Piston.

11. The pistons are of aluminium alloy and have slightly concave heads. Five very shallow cast iron rings are set in grooves near the top of the piston, and oilholes are drilled beneath the lowest ring. The lugs, or bosses, which house the gudgeon pin are cast on the underside of the piston head,

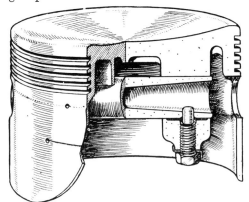

FIG. 7.—PISTON AND GUDGEON PIN, SECTIONED.

instead of being cast on the skirt. The underside of the head is cast with various stiffening webs. Six short radial webs unite the skirt to a circular web concentric with the centre of the head, and this circular web is braced by a straight web at right angles to the gudgeon pin axis. The trailing edge of the skirt is cut away to clear the adjacent and following piston.

Gudgeon Pins.

12.—(i) The hollow steel gudgeon pins are bored at each end with a taper which narrows towards the centre. They are parallel sided and are a hard push fit in the piston bosses when the piston is cold. Each pin is secured at one end by a locking bolt which screws into a tapped hole in one of the bosses; the other is left free to allow for expansion of the piston. The bolt is reduced at the end to enter a radially drilled hole in the gudgeon pin. A special 2-tab washer locks the bolt. It is important to note that only washers conforming to the particular specification for this work may be used; standard washers to A.G.S. specification are not suitable. The washer, which is of sheet steel, must be annealed before use and must be left with particularly full radii at the tabs, as otherwise these will break off.

(ii) Before the adoption of this method of locating the gudgeon pin, a floating type pin was employed and the ends were plugged with aluminium to prevent damage to the cylinder walls. The bore of the bosses was such as to provide a hard push fit for the pin when first assembled, but after a short period of running it became a slacker fit and floated in the piston. The bosses were drilled and grooved for lubrication.

Connecting rods.

13.—(i) The connecting rod assembly is on the Gnome master rod system. All nine rods are of tubular section steel and, with the exception of the master rod, they are bushed with phosphor bronze at both ends. Measuring between centres of the gudgeon pin and crank pin, the master rod is 1mm. shorter than the articulated rods. This is partly to compensate for the discrepancies of the stroke of the articulated rods caused by the obliquity of the master rod. The master rod is bushed with phosphor bronze at its little end, but its big end revolves on two large ball bearings mounted on the crankpin.

(ii) The big end of the master rod is formed with two large hollow flanges which serve as housings for the two ball bearings on the crankpin and are drilled with holes that act as sockets for the eight wristpins of the auxiliary rods. Each wristpin is located in its front socket by a screwed snug, which prevents it from rotating and registers its oil ducts. The lubricating details of the connecting rod assembly are described in para. 34.

FIG. 8.—MASTER ROD AND AUXILIARY ROD WITH PISTONS.

Valves.

14.—(i) The exhaust valves are of the mushroom type, and their smallest diameter is 58 mm. For cooling purposes they are located towards the leading edge of the combustion

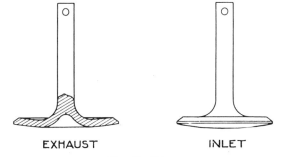

EXHAUST   INLET

FIG. 9.—VALVES.

head. They work in cast iron guides, pressed into light tripod cages made in one piece with the combustion heads. The waste gases pass direct into the cowl.

(ii) The inlet valves, of which the smallest diameter is 52 mm., are of the solid type, and are located towards the trailing edge of the cylinder heads. Their steel guides are pressed into valve boxes made in one piece with the combustion heads.

(iii) The springs of both valves are of the volute type.

87

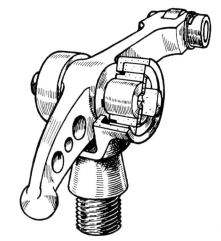

FIG. 10.—VALVE ROCKER AND BRACKET.

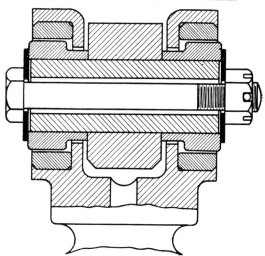

FIG. 11.—SECTION OF VALVE ROCKER MOUNTING.

15. The inlet and exhaust rockers are mounted in short brackets, or supports, screwed into the combustion heads. The upper ends of the brackets are forked and the eyes in the forked ends are bushed with steel. The rocker arms are curved sharply down towards the push rod to clear the camber of the engine cowl. At each end of the rocker fulcrum pin is a steel washer, held in position by the bolt passing through the centre of the hollow pin. Taking the parts from one end, therefore, there is a washer for the inner ring of the ring bearing, the rocking lever, the other inner ring, and the other washer. The washers on the outer ends prevent the inner rings from moving outwards. The outer rings are pushed into the rocking lever housings, the edges of these housings being spun over to secure the rings in position. The construction is clearly shown in figs. 10 and 11.

16. The valve end of each rocker is fitted with a hardened steel roller, working on a hardened pin, secured by a washer and split pin. The outer ends of the rockers are attached to the push rods by ball joints, protected from accidental disengagement by spring clips. The pushrods have screwed adjustments at top and bottom.

Cam gear.

17. The cam gear box consists of a circular steel casing, bolted to the front of the crankcase. It revolves upon two large ball bearings, carried upon the crankshaft extension piece. Between these bearings are the two small bearings on which the inlet and exhaust gears are mounted. Eighteen phosphor bronze guides, each carrying a tappet, are pressed tightly into holes bored through the inner and outer shells of the cam gear box. Each tappet is connected to its pushrod by a ball joint. The cam driving gear is of the Clerget type. Two large internal-toothed rings, known as the inlet and exhaust gear ring respectively, are a tapping fit in a housing formed in the inner flange of the cam gear box.

They are located circumferentially by a key, and spaced by distance studs, the exhaust gear ring being next to the airscrew. These gear rings revolve with the cam gear box, and each has eighteen teeth.

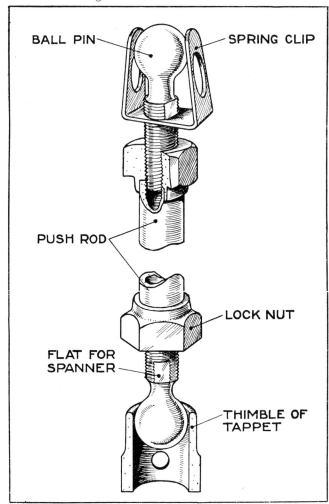

FIG. 12.—DETAILS OF VALVE PUSH ROD.

18. Inside the exhaust and inlet gear rings, and in their respective planes are the externally toothed exhaust and inlet gears, which have sixteen teeth each. These gears are mounted on ball bearings upon the crankshaft extension piece, the inner races of their bearings being eccentric to the crankshaft, so that each gear is mounted eccentrically in relation to each gear ring.

19. To convey oil to the cam gear box a duct is drilled from the crankpin down the front web of the crank and along the crankshaft extension piece; and an oil hole is drilled at right angles to the axis between the inlet and exhaust gears. There is a second hole at the rear of inlet gear, supplied with oil through an oilway or groove cut in the cam gear-shaft key. The oil escaping from these holes is distributed throughout the cam gear box by centrifugal force as the engine rotates.

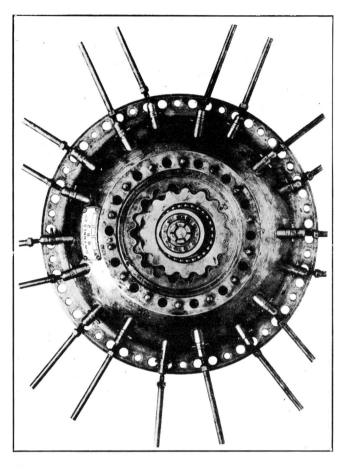

FIG. 13.—CAM GEAR BOX. SHOWING GEARS, TAPPETS AND PUSH RODS.

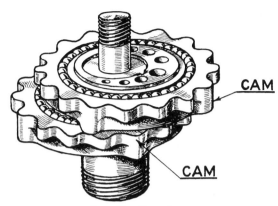

FIG. 15.—CAM GEARS.

Action of the valve gear.

20. The action of the valve gear appears complex at first sight, but is easily understood by following the working of an isolated tappet. Fig. 16 is a diagram prepared for the purpose. F is the selected inlet valve tappet, A is the inlet gear ring (eighteen teeth) revolving with the tappets round the centre B. C is the inlet gear (sixteen teeth) running on ball bearings (not shown) round the centre E. Four cam points 1, 2, 3 and 4, are machined integrally with the gear C. The broken line passing through BEF bisects the arc representing the period for which all nine inlet valves are open.

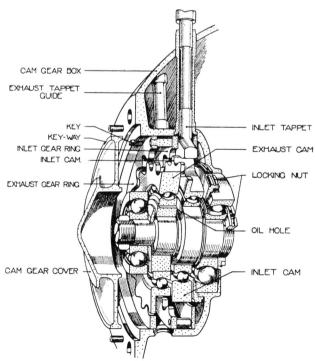

FIG. 14.—VIEW OF CAM GEAR BOX.

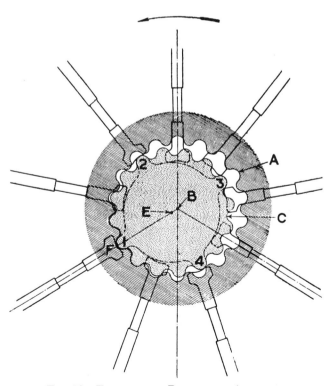

FIG. 16.—EXPLANATORY DIAGRAM OF ACTION OF CAM GEARS.

21. (i) Consider the inlet tappet F, shown fully lifted by the cam point 1. If the gear ring A is turned through one complete revolution in the direction of the arrow, the sixteen-tooth gear C will engage the eighteen-tooth gear ring A, and will therefore complete $1\frac{1}{8}$ revolutions while A completes one revolution. The tappet F, being carried round with A, will also complete one revolution, and will have returned to the position shown; but it will now fall between cam points 1 and 2, because C has turned through $1\frac{1}{8}$ revolutions.

(ii) In the next revolution, the gear C will gain another $\frac{1}{8}$ revolution. At the end of this second revolution the tappet F will again be in the position shown, but will now be fully lifted by the cam point 2, as the cam point is integral with C, which gains $\frac{1}{4}$ of a revlution in two revolutions of A. The tappet F is, therefore, lifted each alternate revolution.

(iii) Further, as the distance between each pair of tappets is $\frac{1}{8}$ of the circumference of the gear ring, i.e., two teeth, and the distance between each pair of cam points is $\frac{1}{4}$ of the circumference of the gear, i.e., four teeth, the cams will operate each alternate tappet in order; the timing sequence will, therefore, be 1, 3, 5, 7, 0, 2, 4, 6, 8.

(iv) The exhaust valves are operated in a similar fashion.

Nosepiece.

22. The nosepiece is formed integral with the airscrew hub and is bolted to the front of the cam gear box. The loose front flange is splined to the hub barrel. Small dowel pins are provided to ensure the correct angular location of the nosepiece in relation to the airscrew and cam box.

Thrust Box.

23. The thrust box consists of a steel disc, provided with an outer rim and a central hub, or sleeve, of considerable diameter. Nine gas holes are drilled in the web of the disc. No separate gasbox is fitted, but a gas chamber is formed in the recessed back of the thrust box, which is closed by means of a circular aluminium coverplate. The outer edge of the coverplate is bolted to the rear of the thrust box rim. A large orifice in the centre of the coverplate slips over the thrust box sleeve, and is pressed against a shoulder on the sleeve by means of a distance piece, against which the distributor disc is screwed up. The coverplate is ribbed, to stiffen it against possible backfires. The rim of the thrust box has nine gas ports machined in it, and the lower elbows of the induction pipes are bolted down over these holes. As the seatings follow the circumference of the thrust box, and are slightly curved, care is needed to ensure a gastight joint between the elbows and their seatings.

24. The sleeve, or hub, at the centre of the thrust box accommodates two journal bearings on which the thrust box rotates. The front bearing is a Skefko with a double row of staggered balls, and the rear bearing an ordinary single row. The thrust bearing is of the single row type, which, owing to the method in which it is mounted, takes thrust in either direction. Its rear race abuts with its outer edge against a shoulder machined inside the thrust box sleeve, and with its inner edge against a distance piece. The front race of the ball thrust abuts with its outer edge against a locking ring, screwed into an internal thread formed in the thrust box sleeve: the inner edge of the front race abuts against a distance piece.

25. Fig. 18 illustrates, in a clear fashion, the action of the thrustrace. As the arrow indicates, a tractor airscrew tends to pull the crankcase along the crankshaft from right to left. The thrustrace has a two-fold purpose, viz. :—

(i) It limits the longitudinal movement.
(ii) It minimises the friction.

A little longitudinal float or play is possible between the thrustrace, the crankshaft and the crankcase, as indicated by the clearances shown at S1 and S2, which are exaggerated in

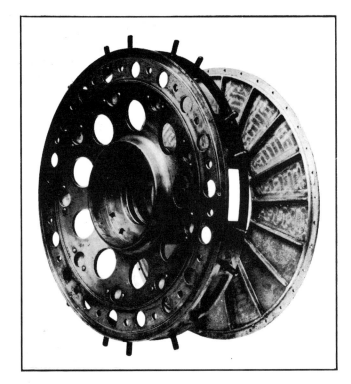

FIG. 17.—THRUST BOX. SHOWING COVER PLATE (DETACHED) ON RIGHT.

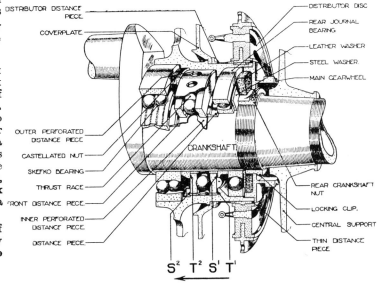

FIG. 18.—SECTIONED VIEW OF THRUSTRACE.

90

the diagram. The tractor airscrew tends to pull the crankcase along the crankshaft in the direction of the arrow. The resultant thrust passes from the crankcase into the thrustrace at the point T1. As soon as this thrust is felt at T1, the other face of the thrustrace comes hard up against the immovable distance piece at T2. Whilst the engine continues to run, no further longitudinal movement takes place. Meanwhile the friction is absorbed inside the thrustrace, and minute clearances exist at S1 and S2. By contrast, if the engine were used as a pusher, these details would be reversed. The thrust would pass from the crankcase into the thrustrace at S1 and further longitudinal movement would be checked at S2; minute clearances would then exist at T1 and T2.

26. A duct drilled through the crankpin web brings oil into the thrust box, where it travels along various small grooves, and is finally distributed throughout the thrust by centrifugal force.

27. The high tension distributor disc slides over the central sleeve of the thrust box : it is positioned axially by distance pieces, and located circumferentially by two keys. It is locked into place by a flange on the threaded spigot of the main gearwheel. This gearwheel, which drives the magnetos and pumps, has an externally threaded spigot, which screws into an internal thread in the rear end of the thrust box sleeve, and its spigot houses a leather oil retaining washer. A locking ring on the crankshaft, provided with a spring locking wire, completes the assembly. Any verbal description of this unit is necessarily complicated, but a study of figs. 18 and 38 should make the details intelligible.

Central support.

28. The central support consists of a flanged steel disc, with a tapered boss at its centre. The support does not take the main pull of the engine, but carries its weight, supports the auxiliary fittings, and aligns the crankshaft. A special coupling, described in para. 4, draws the crankshaft into the taper hub at the centre of the support, two keys serving to locate the shaft, so that its crank is always vertical, provided that the central support is properly assembled with its ring plate in the fuselage. This coupling also pushes the crankshaft out of the taper hub when the engine is dismantled. Seven holes are drilled in the plate or web portion of the support. Through four of these holes the driven pinions of the magnetos, and the two pumps are passed to mesh with the main gearwheel on the thrust box. Two of the remaining holes accommodate the two carbon brush holders, and the other hole accommodates a starting brush when required. Suitable brackets for supporting the magnetos and pumps are provided on the back plate.

Ignition.

29. Ignition is provided by two M.L. magnetos of the revolving armature type, giving two sparks a revolution. Being geared to make nine armature revolutions for four revolutions of the engine, they furnish eighteen sparks every four engine revolutions. or nine sparks every two engine revolutions, which is the number required for a nine-cylinder engine of the four-stroke type. The firing order is 1, 3, 5, 7, 0, 2, 4, 6, 8. Each magneto supplies a separate set of sparking

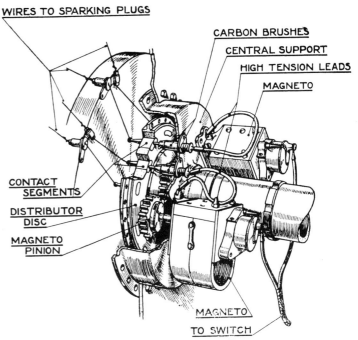

FIG. 19.—SECTIONED VIEW OF DISTRIBUTOR.

FIG. 20.—REAR VIEW OF ENGINE.

91

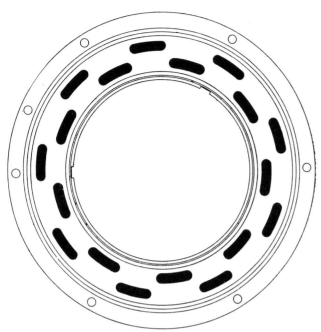

FIG. 21.—DISTRIBUTOR DISC. SHOWING ARRANGEMENT OF CONTACT SEGMENTS.

plugs, and the circuit is as follows : The high-tension current is picked up by a carbon brush from the collector ring on the armature and is led by a cable to a terminal fixed in an insulated holder on the (stationary) backplate of the centre support. From this terminal the current passes into a carbon brush that is pressed by a light spring against the revolving distributor disc on the thrustbox. On the distributor disc there are two concentric circles of nine insulated contact segments apiece (fig. 21), the inner ring of contacts registering with the lower brush, and the outer ring with the outer brush. On the other, or front, side of the distributor disc are eighteen terminals, each electrically connected to a corresponding contact on the rear of the disc. These terminals are mounted in two concentric circles of nine terminals each, those in the outer cicrcle being slightly the longer. Naked brass wires run from these terminals to insulator brackets on the outer periphery of the thrustbox : loops in the ends of the lower wires are coupled by naked wires of lighter section to the sparking plugs. The wires to the sparking plugs are

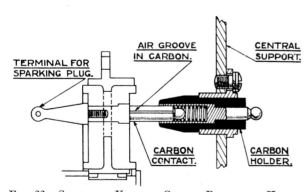

FIG. 22.—SECTIONED VIEW OF CARBON BRUSH AND HOLDER.

supported in insulated clips, each pair of insulators being supported by one bracket. The arrangement of the wires and insulators is shown in fig. 36.

Oil pumps.

30. A Le Rhone type oil pump is fitted. It is mounted on the back of the central support, and driven by a pinion meshing with the large gearwheel on the thrustbox. It is geared down to about one-third engine speed by means of a worm and worm wheel inside the pump casing. The worm-wheel shaft is formed with a crank from which a connecting rod and piston of an oscillating cylinder are actuated. The cylinder is mounted in trunnions set half-way up its outer walls. The trunnions are carried in bearings in the body and the cover of the pump. One of the bearings contains a spring, which serves to maintain surface contact, and an oil-tight joint between a machined surface on the side of the cylinder and the pump cover.

31.—(i) A small valve port is drilled in this machined surface. As the cylinder oscillates, the flat on the cylinder head swings through a small arc against a face plate formed on the bronze cover of the pump, and the valve port alternately registers with two oil leads in the cover, one of which is an intake and the other a delivery. The oil from the tank enters the pump casing by gravity and is led by a catchpit and trough to the intake hole with which the valve port registers at the commencement of the suction stroke. The cylinder fills up with oil and swings away from the intake lead ; as the piston begins its delivery stroke, the movement of the cylinder registers the valve port with the delivery hole, which is simply a hole drilled through the pump cover. A junction box, outside the cover, provides connections for pipes leading to the crankshaft, pulsator and air pump.

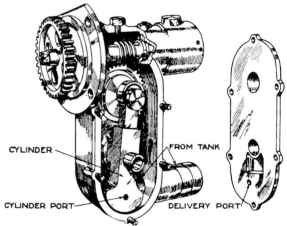

FIG. 23.—VIEW OF OIL PUMP.

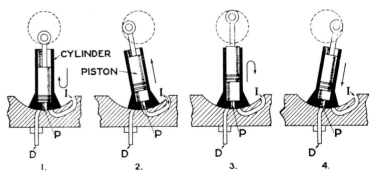

FIG. 24.—DIAGRAM ILLUSTRATING ACTION OF OIL PUMP.

(ii) The above sketch is purely diagrammatic : the three ports are actually at one side and not at the bottom as shown.

I = Intake port in casing. D = Delivery port in casing.
P = Port in cylinder.

(a) Piston ascending for intake stroke : cylinder swinging to the right for P to register with I.

(b) Intake stroke : P and I registered with each other.

(c) Cylinder swinging toward the left for delivery stroke; piston ready to descend.

(d) Delivery stroke : P and D registered : piston forcing oil out of cylinder.

Lubrication system.

32. The delivery pipe from the oil pump leads to a hole in the crankshaft immediately behind the central support. A copper pipe inside the crankshaft conducts the oil to a duct in the base of the rear web of the hollow crankpin (fig. 25). The register of the oil holes in the central support and the crank must be carefully tested when spares are fitted.

Supply to the thrustbox.

33. Just above the junction between the pipe and the crankpin web, a by-pass conveys oil to a longitudinal groove, cut along the top of the crankshaft, which extends to the rear, as far back as the rear journal ball bearing. From this groove the oil passes up grooves cut radially in the rear faces of the front distance piece and of the back distance piece. Centrifugal force then flings the oil thus liberated over the interior of the thrustbox.

Lubrication of the connecting rod assembly.

34. This demands particular attention, as the effect of centrifugal force tends to swirl the oil away from the centre of the engine, and rather complex arrangements are needed to ensure an adequate supply. The oil passes up the duct A (fig. 26), in the rear crank web, and along a duct in the crankpin. A hole, B, drilled at right angles to the crankpin axis, conducts a liberal supply of oil into the annular space, C, between the crankpin and the inner diameter of the big end of the master rod. This oil is directed to a number of outlets, all of which are shown in fig. 26. From the annular space the oil reaches two circumferential gutters, EE, cut in the inner diameters of the flanges of the big end of the master rod. Each of these gutters is drilled with eight holes, GG, leading through into the sockets in which the wristpins are mounted; corresponding holes, HH, in the wrist pins themselves are accurately registered by means of the pin stops in the wrist pins. Thus an oil supply is assured to both ends of each wrist pin. The register of the oil holes in the wrist pins must be carefully verified whenever any spares are fitted.

35. An oil chamber is formed in both ends of each wrist pin; the rear end of the wrist pin is solid, and the front end is sealed by a screwed brass plug, the end of which forms a partition between the two oil chambers, JJ, inside the wrist pin (see fig. 26). These two oil chambers are filled with oil from the circumferential gutters, EE, by the leads and holes, GG and HH. The brass plug must be screwed tightly home as otherwise leakage will occur at this point. From each oil chamber a duct, K, drilled in the wrist pin at right angles to its axis, conveys oil into grooves cut on the outer surface of the wrist pin, from which oil is distributed round that end of the phosphor bronze bush. Thus both ends of each bush possess a separate oil supply.

36. There is, further, a separate oil supply to the centre of each wrist pin and bush. Holes, LL, are drilled in the central barrel of the master rod big end, which forms the wall of the main annular oil space, C. The oil is sprayed under pressure from these holes, which are opposite the centres of the big ends of the auxiliary connecting rods. Slots are cut in these big ends opposite the spray holes; the oil enters the slots, and passes round circumferential grooves

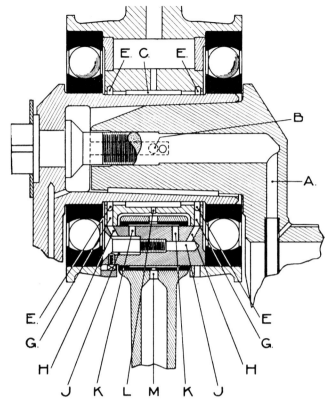

FIG. 26.—LUBRICATION OF CONNECTING ROD ASSEMBLY.

A   Duct in rear web of crank.
B   Oil hole from A to
C   Annular space between crankpin and big end.
EE Circumferential gutters in flanges of master rod big end.
GG Oil holes from the gutters to the right wristpin sockets.
HH Holes in wristpin sockets registering with EE.
JJ Oil chambers in ends of wristpins.
KK Holes conveying oil from JJ to the auxiliary big end bushes.
LL Oil spraying holes in the master rod big end which forms the outer wall of the annular space C.
M   Hole through which oil enters the hollow auxiliary connecting rods.

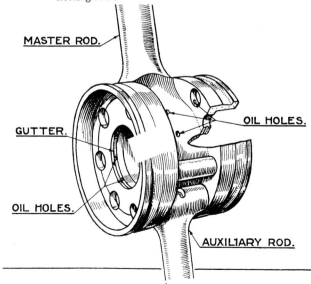

FIG. 27.—LUBRICATION OF MASTER ROD ASSEMBLY.

cut in the bushes. Holes, M, are drilled in these grooves opposite the tubular connecting rods, and centrifugal force flings the oil up the hollow rods. It passes up the tubular rods into the gudgeon pin bush, the oil which escapes from the gudgeon pin bush passing into the piston. A ring of oil holes is drilled round the piston skirt, just below its head, through which this oil passes on to the cylinder walls; it is joined in the cylinders and pistons by any oil which escapes from the nine big end bearings at the centre of the engine.

Supply to the cam gear box.

37. A by-pass from the crankpin conducts some of the oil supply to a duct down the hollow front crank web, and so into the extension shaft. It emerges between the cam gears and at the rear of the inlet cam ring, through holes drilled approximately at right angles to the shaft axis, and is distributed throughout the interior of the cam gear box by centrifugal force.

Air pump.

38. The air pump, for providing pressure for the petrol system, is not a standard fitting, but is available if required. When not fitted, the hole in the main support is blanked off, and the oil lead in the four-way junction box is capped. When fitted, the pump is mounted on the rear of the centre support, its pinion meshing with the large gearwheel on the thrustbox. It is geared down by a worm and wormwheel enclosed in its casing. The wormwheel shaft terminates in a crank which actuates a connecting rod and piston in the ordinary way. The cylinder is of steel, with cooling fins machined on the exterior of its barrel, and the air intake ports consist of four holes cut in the cylinder wall immediately above the lowest position of the piston head. During the

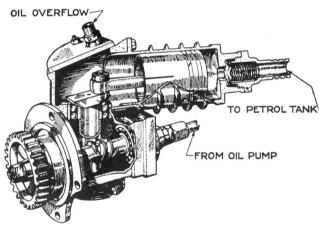

FIG. 28.—AIR PUMP.

brief period for which these ports are uncovered by the piston, the suction which has previously accumulated in the cylinder induces a rush of air; this air is compressed by the piston as it rises. Towards the top of the stroke the pressure opens a spring disc non-return valve, communicating with the pressure pipe to the tanks. The piston, which is of aluminium, is fitted with two rings and is slotted at the skirt.

The pump is oiled through a special connection from the junction box outside the oil pump. The position of the oil entry and the provision of an overflow (fig. 28) obviate all danger of the air pump becoming flooded with oil. The four-way fitting (fig. 29) must be assembled as shown, so that the correct branch registers with the connection to the air pump. This is important, as the hole in this branch is carefully dimensioned.

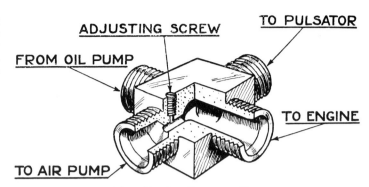

FIG. 29.—OIL JUNCTION BOX.

Induction system.

39—(i) The carburettor is screwed on to the extreme rear of the long end of the crankshaft, and the explosive mixture passes through the hollow crankshaft into the main crankcase. It is then sucked through the gas holes in the steel web of the thrustbox, and passes into the gas chamber surrounding the thrustbox, which is closed by an aluminium cover plate as shown in fig. 17. The lower elbows of the induction pipes are bolted to rectangular orifices cut in the rim of the thrustbox, and the upper elbows of the pipes are bolted to induction pockets machined in one with the cylinder heads. The induction pipes consist of upper and lower elbows, secured by the taped joints, shown in fig. 30, to straight lengths of aluminium tubing.

(ii) Approximately thirteen feet of tape are required for each joint. The tape is taken through the slot and halfway round the groove A. A drop of lubricating oil is then put on each bearing surface B to prevent the pipe seizing. A blob of seccotine is placed on the inner end of the tape to make it

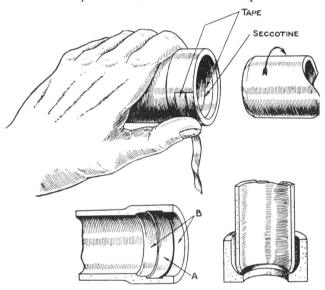

FIG. 30.—TAPED JOINT FOR INDUCTION PIPE.

adhere to the pipe which is twisted in a clockwise direction until practically all the tape is wound in. Care must be taken to keep the tape flat and taut during the winding process, by holding the thumb against it as shown. To remove the pipe, a little lubricating oil should be put on the end of the tape (which projects through the slot) and allowed to soak in. This usually suffices to ease the joint. The ends of the pipe are slightly reduced in diameter; if a spare is received with unreduced ends, the pipe may be lightly tapped into a cup shaped jig as shown in fig. 30. The bends in the pipe must be set so that they are fair before screwing into place.

Carburettor.

40. The Bloctube type of carburetter is illustrated in figs. 31 and 32. Its body consists of a short extension, screwed to the rear end of the long crank. This extension houses the jet and throttle slide, which constitute the vital parts of the carburettor. The rear end of the body is fitted with a lug in which the airpipes are secured. The jet projects horizontally at right angles into the tubular body of the carburettor, and is immediately opposite the throttle slide. A tapered needle is mounted in the end of the throttle slide

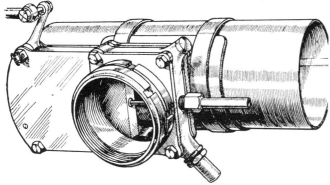

FIG. 31.—BLOCTUBE CARBURETTOR.

in line with the jet axis. As the throttle slide is moved to and fro, the taper needle is plunged further into the jet, or withdrawn from it, as the case may be, thus varying its effective aperture.

41. The throttle is a brass slide, mounted in guides to move horizontally at right angles across the tubular body of the carburettor. In shape it resembles a shallow box, set on edge : the face furthest from the engine is hinged, and is tightly pressed against the guiding slide by an internal spring, so as to make a gastight joint. Unions for petrol drainpipes are provided below the mixing chamber.

Fine adjustment valve.

42. An auxiliary device, known as a fine adjustment valve, is always used in conjunction with a Bloctube carburetter. This valve serves several purposes. In conjunction with the variable jet it enables the pilot to adjust the mixture to varying conditions. It provides a form of altitude control, permitting the supply of petrol to be substantially reduced at great heights. Finally, it embodies a petrol filter. Its detailed construction is clearly shown in fig. 33. It is controlled by a separate lever, placed alongside the throttle lever in the cockpit.

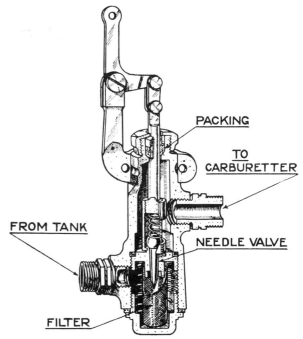

FIG. 33.—FINE ADJUSTMENT VALVE.

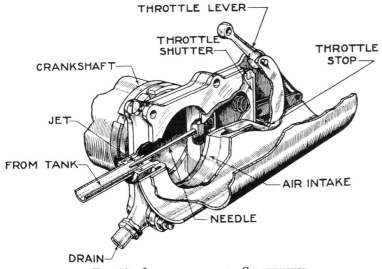

FIG. 32.—INTERNAL VIEW OF CARBURETTOR.